MEETING THE
CALIFORNIA
CHALLENGE

Instruction and Practice for High School Students on the California Mathematics Content Standards

GLOBE FEARON
Pearson Learning Group

ISBN 0-130-23943-7

Printed in the United States of America

2 3 4 5 6 7 8 9 10   05 04 03

Globe
Fearon

Pearson Learning Group

1-800-321-3106
www.pearsonlearning.com

Contents

Chapter 3   Measurement and Geometry

Chapter 4   Statistics, Data Analysis, and Probability

Chapter 5   Mathematical Reasoning

Glossary

To the Student

Meeting the California Challenge was created to help you master the key elements of the California content standards in mathematics. As you complete each lesson, you will increase your competence in mathematics and gain confidence in your abilities.

About This Book

This book is organized into 60 lessons. Each lesson will help you understand a skill related to one or more of the five main content areas: number sense; algebra and functions; measurement and geometry; statistics, data analysis, and probability; and mathematical reasoning.

Each lesson begins with instruction. The instruction includes several examples and one or two self-test items with explanations. Following the instruction are multiple-choice questions that target the concepts and skills of the lesson.

The lessons expand on prerequisite knowledge as you navigate through each chapter and within the book. Your teacher can refer you to lessons that you may need to review to obtain prerequisite skills.

On pages 243–247, you will find a glossary, which includes definitions of most key terms.

How You Will Use This Book

To help you review and sharpen your skills, your teacher will give assignments from this book. If you have difficulty with particular lessons, consult your teacher. He or she may give you additional strategies and practices that may help.

Determining Absolute Value and Opposites

LESSON 1

You will learn how to find:
• the opposite of a number
• the absolute value of a number

Key Words: number line, negative number, zero, positive number, opposite, absolute value

A thermometer is a model of a vertical *number line*.

Suppose it was 5° above zero on a certain afternoon, then 5° below zero later that evening. These temperatures can be represented on a horizontal number line as 5 and −5.

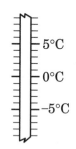

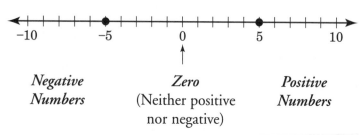

Negative Numbers   *Zero* (Neither positive nor negative)   *Positive Numbers*

Numbers such as 5 and −5 are called opposites. *Opposites* are a pair of numbers that are the same distance from zero and on opposite sides of zero on a number line. The number line below shows several pairs of opposites.

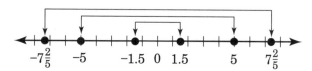

Here are some important facts about opposites:

• The opposite of a positive number is negative.

• The opposite of a negative number is positive.

• Zero has no opposite.

• The symbol for opposite is the same as the symbol for negative.

You can read −5 as "negative 5" or "the opposite of 5" because they indicate the same number. The expression −(−5) is read "the opposite of negative 5." To simplify, write −(−5) = 5.

Lesson 1: Determining Absolute Value and Opposites

Example	How to read it	Simplest form
-10	The opposite of 10, or negative 10	-10
$-(-10)$	The opposite of negative 10	10
$-2\frac{3}{4}$	The opposite of $2\frac{3}{4}$, or negative $2\frac{3}{4}$	$-2\frac{3}{4}$
$-(-2\frac{3}{4})$	The opposite of negative $2\frac{3}{4}$	$2\frac{3}{4}$

The absolute value of x is x if $x \geq 0$.

The absolute value of x is $-x$ if $x < 0$.

The *absolute value* of a number can be thought of as that number's distance from zero. The numbers 5 and -5 are each 5 units from zero, so they each have absolute value 5. To symbolize the absolute value of a number, you write the number between two small vertical lines.

Write: $|5| = 5$ Say: "The absolute value of five is five."

Write: $|-5| = 5$ Say: "The absolute value of negative five is five."

Notice that a number and its opposite have the same absolute value. Because a distance cannot be negative, an absolute value cannot be negative.

Examples: $|-6| = 6$ $\left|-3\frac{2}{7}\right| = 3\frac{2}{7}$ $|100.9| = 100.9$ $|0| = 0$

Self-Test

Circle the letter of the correct answer.
Which of the following statements is true?

A. The absolute value of a number must be negative.

B. The absolute value of a number must be positive.

C. The absolute value of a number cannot be zero.

D. The absolute value of a number cannot be negative.

Check your answer.

D is correct. The absolute value of a number is that number's distance from zero, and a distance cannot be negative, so this statement is true. The absolute value of zero is zero, which is neither negative nor positive.

Practice

9/10 ☺

Determining Absolute Value and Opposites

Circle the letter of the correct answer.

1. Which of the following statements is true?

   (A.) A number and its opposite are the same distance from zero on a number line.

   B. The opposite of a number must be negative.

   C. The absolute value of a number must be negative.

   D. The absolute value of a positive number is negative.

2. What does the following represent? $-|3.7|$

   (A) the opposite of the absolute value of 3.7

   B. the absolute value of 3.7

   C. the opposite of negative 3.7

   D. 3.7

3. Which of the following numbers is equal to $-|3.7|$?

   (A.) -3.7

   B. 0.37

   C. $-(-3.7)$

   D. 3.7

4. Which of the following numbers is the opposite of $\frac{2}{5}$?

   A. $-\frac{5}{2}$

   (B.) $-\frac{2}{5}$

   C. $\frac{2}{5}$

   D. $\frac{5}{2}$

5. Which of the following is a correct way to read the number -1.1?

   A. the absolute value of 1.1

   B. the opposite of negative 1.1

   C. the absolute value of the opposite of 1.1

   (D.) negative 1.1

6. Which of the following numbers is equal to $|-2|$?

   A. -2

   B. $-\frac{1}{2}$

   C. $\frac{1}{2}$

   (D.) 2

7. Which of the following numbers is the opposite of negative ten?

   A. -10

   B. $-\frac{1}{10}$

   C. $\frac{1}{10}$

   (D.) 10

8. Which of the following numbers is equal to $-|-7|$?

   (A.) -7

   B. 0

   C. $\frac{1}{7}$

   D. 7

9. $\left|3\frac{1}{3}\right| =$

   A. $-3\frac{1}{3}$

   B. 0.33

   C. $3\frac{3}{10}$

   (D.) $3\frac{1}{3}$

10. The absolute value of any number is:

    A. zero

    (B.) the same as the opposite of the number

    C. negative if the number is positive

    D. the distance of the number from zero on a number line

Lesson 1: Determining Absolute Value and Opposites

11. Which of the following numbers has the same value as the absolute value of -8?

A. -8
B. -0.8
C. 0.8
D. 8

12. Which of the following numbers is the opposite of 107.1?

A. -107.1
B. $\frac{1}{107.1}$
C. $|107.1|$
D. 107.1

13. Simplify the number shown below.
$|-44|$

A. -44
B. $\frac{1}{44}$
C. $\frac{10}{44}$
D. 44

14. Simplify the number shown below.
$-(-1)$

A. -1
B. $-\frac{1}{1}$
C. $\frac{1}{10}$
D. 1

15. Which of the following is a correct way to read the number $-(-4)$?

A. the opposite of 4
B. the opposite of the absolute value of 4
C. the opposite of negative 4
D. negative 4

16. If two different numbers are the same distance from zero on a number line, then:

A. they are equal to each other
B. they are opposites of each other
C. they are on the same side of zero
D. one number is half the other number

17. The opposite of a number:

A. may be equal to the number
B. must be on the same side of zero as the number
C. has the same absolute value as the number
D. must be negative

18. The opposite of negative 5, in simplest form, is:

A. -5
B. $-(5)$
C. (-5)
D. 5

19. $-|-52| =$

A. $-(-52)$
B. -52
C. 52
D. $|-52|$

20. $-(11\frac{6}{7}) =$

A. $-11\frac{6}{7}$
B. $-(-11\frac{6}{7})$
C. $|-11\frac{6}{7}|$
D. $11\frac{6}{7}$

Adding and Subtracting Rational Numbers

LESSON 2

You will learn how to:
- add and subtract integers, fractions, and decimals

Key Words: add, subtract, prime factor, least common multiple

There are two rules that can be used to **add** any two numbers.

If the numbers have the same sign → Add their absolute values; the sum has the sign of the two numbers.

If the numbers have different signs → Subtract their absolute values; the sum has the sign of the number with the larger absolute value.

Examples	Add or subtract the absolute values	Determine the sign	Add
$2 + 5$	$\lvert 2 \rvert + \lvert 5 \rvert = 2 + 5 = 7$	The sum is positive because both numbers are positive.	$2 + 5 = 7$
$-2 + (-5)$	$\lvert -2 \rvert + \lvert -5 \rvert = 2 + 5 = 7$	The sum is negative because both numbers are negative.	$-2 + (-5) = -7$
$-\frac{1}{8} + (-11\frac{3}{8})$	$\lvert -\frac{1}{8} \rvert + \lvert -11\frac{3}{8} \rvert = \frac{1}{8} + 11\frac{3}{8}$ $= 11\frac{4}{8} = 11\frac{1}{2}$	The sum is negative because both numbers are negative.	$-\frac{1}{8} + (-11\frac{3}{8}) = -11\frac{1}{2}$
$2 + -5$	$\lvert 2 \rvert = 2,\ \lvert -5 \rvert = 5$ $5 - 2 = 3$	The sum is negative because $\lvert -5 \rvert$ is larger than $\lvert 2 \rvert$.	$2 + (-5) = -3$
$-2 + 5$	$\lvert -2 \rvert = 2,\ \lvert 5 \rvert = 5$ $5 - 2 = 3$	The sum is positive because $\lvert 5 \rvert$ is larger than $\lvert -2 \rvert$.	$-2 + 5 = 3$
$0.036 + (-21.1)$	$\lvert 0.036 \rvert = 0.036$ $\lvert -21.1 \rvert = 21.1$ $\begin{array}{r} 21.100 \\ -\ 0.036 \\ \hline 21.064 \end{array}$	The sum is negative because $\lvert -21.1 \rvert$ is larger than $\lvert 0.036 \rvert$.	$0.036 + (-21.1) = -21.064$

To *subtract* a number, add its opposite.

Examples	Determine the opposite	Add the opposite
$5 - 3$	The opposite of 3 is -3.	$5 - 3 = 5 + (-3) = 2$
$-7 - 4$	The opposite of 4 is -4.	$-7 - 4 = -7 + (-4) = -11$
$8 - (-2)$	The opposite of -2 is 2.	$8 - (-2) = 8 + 2 = 10$
$-6 - (-1)$	The opposite of -1 is 1.	$-6 - (-1) = -6 + 1 = -5$
$-\frac{3}{4} - \frac{1}{4}$	The opposite of $\frac{1}{4}$ is $-\frac{1}{4}$.	$-\frac{3}{4} - \frac{1}{4} = -\frac{3}{4} + (-\frac{1}{4}) = -\frac{4}{4} = -1$ Remember that to add fractions with like denominators, you add the numerators and keep the same denominator.
$60 - (-5.55)$	The opposite of -5.55 is 5.55.	$60 - (-5.55) = 60 + 5.55 = 65.55$

To add or subtract fractions with unlike denominators, you need a common denominator.

Example: $\frac{1}{12} + \frac{5}{18}$

Factor each denominator into prime factors. A *prime factor* has no factors other than one and itself. $\rightarrow$ $12 = 2 \cdot 2 \cdot 3$ $18 = 2 \cdot 3 \cdot 3$

Form the *least common multiple* (LCM) of 12 and 18 by using each different factor the greatest number of times it appears in either factorization.

$$12 = 2 \cdot 2 \cdot 3 \qquad 18 = 2 \cdot 3 \cdot 3 \qquad LCM = 2 \cdot 2 \cdot 3 \cdot 3 = 36$$

Rename the fractions to be added so that they each have the LCM as a common denominator, then add.

$\frac{1}{12} = \frac{1}{12} \cdot \frac{3}{3} = \frac{3}{36}$ $\qquad$ $\frac{5}{18} = \frac{5}{18} \cdot \frac{2}{2} = \frac{10}{36}$ $\qquad$ Remember that $\frac{3}{3} = 1$ and $\frac{2}{2} = 1$, so the values of the fractions have not changed.

$\frac{1}{12} + \frac{5}{18} = \frac{3}{36} + \frac{10}{36} = \frac{13}{36}$

Self-Test

Circle the letter of the correct answer.

$(-4) + (-1) =$

Ⓐ -5 $\qquad\qquad$ C. 3

B. -3 $\qquad\qquad$ D. 5

Check your answer.

A is correct. Because (-4) and (-1) have the same sign, add their absolute values. $|-4| + |-1| = 4 + 1 = 5$. *The sum is negative because both numbers are negative.* $(-4) + (-1) = -5$.

Practice

Adding and Subtracting Rational Numbers

17/20

Circle the letter of the correct answer.

1. $7 + (-4) =$

   A. -11

   B. -3

   C. 3 *(circled)*

   D. 11

2. $10 - (-20) =$

   A. -30

   B. -10

   C. 10

   D. 30 *(circled)*

3. $\frac{1}{2} - \frac{3}{4} =$

   A. $-1\frac{1}{4}$

   B. $-\frac{1}{4}$ *(circled)*

   C. $\frac{1}{4}$

   D. $1\frac{1}{4}$

4. Which of the following expressions results in a positive number?

   A. $(-9) + (7) + (1)$

   B. $(5) + (-5) + (-5)$

   C. $(4) + (-1) + (-2)$ *(circled)*

   D. $(-1) + (-3) + 1$

5. $4.2 - 6.2 =$

   A. -10.4

   B. -2.0 *(circled)*

   C. -0.2

   D. 2.0

6. $-2.2 + 3 =$

   A. -6.6

   B. -5.2

   C. 0.8 *(circled)*

   D. 5.2

7. Which of the following expressions results in a negative number?

   A. $(-4) + (6) + (-2)$

   B. $(-4) + (4) + (-2)$ *(circled)*

   C. $(4) + (-2) + (-2)$

   D. $(-4) + (6) + 0$

8. $-\frac{1}{5} - \frac{2}{5} =$ NO.

   A. $-\frac{3}{5}$

   B. $-\frac{3}{10}$ *(circled)*

   C. $\frac{2}{5}$

   D. $\frac{3}{5}$ *(circled)*

9. $-8 + (-1) =$

   A. -9 *(circled)*

   B. -8

   C. -7

   D. 7

10. $-1 - (-2) =$

   A. -3

   B. -1

   C. 1 *(circled)*

   D. 3

Lesson 2: Adding and Subtracting Rational Numbers

11. Which of the following expressions results in a negative number?

   A. $(8) + (-8) + (-8)$
   B. $(-3) + (9) + (-2)$
   C. $(-6) + (2) + (6)$
   D. $(8) + (1) + 0$

12. $1 + (-14) =$

   A. -14
   B. -13
   C. 13
   D. 15

13. $\frac{1}{10} - \frac{3}{10} =$

   A. $-\frac{2}{5}$
   B. $-\frac{3}{10}$
   C. $-\frac{1}{5}$
   D. $\frac{2}{5}$

14. $-\frac{5}{12} + \frac{1}{8} =$

   A. $-\frac{13}{24}$
   B. $-\frac{7}{24}$
   C. $-\frac{5}{24}$
   D. $-\frac{4}{24}$

15. $20 - 21 =$

   A. -41
   B. -1
   C. 1
   D. 41

16. $-1.25 - (-3.75) =$

   A. -5.00
   B. 2.50
   C. 4.25
   D. 5.00

17. $1 + (-12) =$

   A. -13
   B. -12
   C. -11
   D. -10

18. Which of the following expressions has the value zero?

   A. $(9) + (-1) + (-9)$
   B. $(-7) + (9) + (-2)$
   C. $(-2) + (2) + (-1)$
   D. $(-3) + (1) + (-2)$

19. $10 - (-1) =$

   A. -11
   B. -9
   C. 9
   D. 11

20. $-2 - (-2) =$

   A. -4
   B. -2
   C. 0
   D. 4

Multiplying and Dividing Rational Numbers

LESSON 3

You will learn how to:
- multiply and divide integers, fractions, and decimals

Key Words: multiplication, product, division, quotient, reciprocal

There are different ways to indicate *multiplication*.

the *product* of 3 and 5

3 times 5

3×5

$3 \cdot 5$

$(3)(5)$

$3(5)$

$(3)5$

To multiply or divide any two nonzero $\rightarrow$ numbers you can use this rule.

There are different ways to indicate *division*.

the *quotient* of 20 and 4

20 divided by 4

$20 \div 4$

$\frac{20}{4}$

$4\overline{)20}$

If the numbers have the same sign, the answer is positive.

If the numbers have different signs, the answer is negative.

Examples:

Numbers with the same sign

$(3)(5) = 15$

$(-3)(-5) = 15$

$20 \div 4 = 5$

$(-20) \div (-4) = 5$

Numbers with different signs

$(-3)(5) = -15$

$(3)(-5) = -15$

$20 \div (-4) = -5$

$-20 \div 4 = -5$

Multiplying and dividing with zero

The product of zero and any number is zero. $\rightarrow$

The quotient of zero divided by any nonzero number is zero. $\rightarrow$

The quotient of any number divided by zero is undefined. $\rightarrow$

Examples

$(-11)(0)$, 0×21.6, and $0(0)$ all equal 0

$\frac{0}{12}$ and $0 \div (-7)$ both equal 0

$\frac{12}{0}$, $(-7) \div 0$, and $\frac{0}{0}$ are all undefined.

Helpful Hint   For numbers that are not easy to work with, perform the calculation with absolute values, and then determine the sign of the answer.

Reminder   Convert any mixed number or whole number to an improper fraction before you multiply or divide.

Examples: $6 = \frac{6}{1}$ $2\frac{1}{7} = \frac{(2 \times 7) + 1}{7} = \frac{15}{7}$

Examples:

Multiply.	Use absolute values. Simplify if possible.	Determine the sign of the answer.	Write the product.
$-\frac{1}{2} \times \frac{6}{7}$	$\frac{1}{2} \times \frac{6}{7} = \frac{1 \times 6}{2 \times 7} = \frac{6}{14} = \frac{3}{7}$	negative (numbers have different signs)	$-\frac{1}{2} \times \frac{6}{7} = -\frac{3}{7}$
$-3 \times (-\frac{2}{3})$	$3 \times \frac{2}{3} = \frac{3}{1} \times \frac{2}{3} = \frac{6}{3} = 2$	positive (numbers have same sign)	$-3 \times (-\frac{2}{3}) = 2$
$(0.02)(-2.1)$	$\begin{array}{r} 2.1 \leftarrow \text{1 decimal place} \\ \times\ 0.02 \leftarrow \text{2 decimal places} \\ \hline 0.042 \leftarrow \text{3 decimal places} \end{array}$	negative (numbers have different signs)	$(0.02)(-2.1) = -0.042$
$2\frac{1}{3} \cdot \frac{2}{5}$	$2\frac{1}{3} \times \frac{2}{5} = \frac{7}{3} \times \frac{2}{5} = \frac{7 \times 2}{3 \times 5} = \frac{14}{15}$	positive (numbers have same sign)	$2\frac{1}{3} \cdot \frac{2}{5} = \frac{14}{15}$

Two numbers are *reciprocals* if their product is 1.

To divide by a fraction, multiply by its reciprocal.

To divide by a decimal, make the divisor a whole number by moving the decimal point to the right and then move the decimal point in the dividend the same number of places to the right. Write the decimal point in the quotient directly above the decimal point in the dividend.

Examples: $\quad \frac{0.24}{0.2} \quad \rightarrow \quad 0.2\overline{)0.2\ 4}^{\ 1.2}$

Example:

Divide.	Use absolute values. Simplify if possible.	Determine the sign of the answer.	Write the quotient.
$-\frac{1}{2} \div \frac{1}{8}$	$\frac{1}{2} \div \frac{1}{8} = \frac{1}{2} \times \frac{8}{1} = \frac{1 \times 8}{2 \times 1} = \frac{8}{2} = 4$	negative (numbers have different signs)	$-\frac{1}{2} \div \frac{1}{8} = -4$
$\frac{2}{3} \div 2\frac{3}{4}$	$\frac{2}{3} \div 2\frac{3}{4} = \frac{2}{3} \div \frac{11}{4} = \frac{2}{3} \times \frac{4}{11} = \frac{2 \times 4}{3 \times 11} = \frac{8}{33}$	positive (numbers have same sign)	$\frac{2}{3} \div 2\frac{3}{4} = \frac{8}{33}$

Self-Test

Circle the letter of the correct answer.

$-\frac{1}{4} \div -\frac{1}{2} =$

A. -2

B. $-\frac{1}{2}$

C. $\frac{1}{2}$

D. 2

Check your answer.

C is correct.

$\frac{1}{4} \div \frac{1}{2} = \frac{1}{4} \times \frac{2}{1} = \frac{1 \times 2}{4 \times 1} = \frac{2}{4} = \frac{1}{2}$

The quotient is positive because the numbers have the same sign. $-\frac{1}{4} \div -\frac{1}{2} = \frac{1}{2}$

Lesson 3: Multiplying and Dividing Rational Numbers

Practice

Multiplying and Dividing Rational Numbers

Circle the letter of the correct answer.

1. $7 \times (-3) =$

   (A.) -21

   B. -4

   C. 10

   D. 21

2. $-0.36 \div 0.9 =$

   (A.) -0.4

   B. -0.27

   C. 0.27

   D. 0.45

3. $-\frac{2}{7} \times -\frac{4}{5} =$

   A. $-\frac{8}{35}$

   B. $\frac{6}{35}$

   (C.) $\frac{8}{35}$

   D. $\frac{1}{2}$

4. $-75 \div (-15) =$

   A. -5

   B. -3

   (C.) 5

   D. 6

5. $0.3 \times (-0.9) =$

   A. -0.6

   (B.) -0.27

   C. 0.27

   D. 1.2

6. $\frac{1}{9} \div -\frac{2}{3} =$

   A. -9

   B. -6

   (C.) $-\frac{1}{6}$

   D. $-\frac{1}{9}$

$$\frac{1}{9} \div -\frac{2}{3}$$
$$\frac{1}{9} \times -\frac{3}{2} = -\frac{3}{18} = -\frac{1}{6}$$

7. $-\frac{2}{3} \times 2\frac{1}{5} =$

   (A.) $-2\frac{2}{15}$

   B. $-1\frac{7}{15}$

   C. $1\frac{2}{15}$

   D. $2\frac{7}{15}$

8. $-1.6 \div -0.2 =$

   A. -8

   B. -0.8

   C. 0.8

   (D.) 8

9. $\frac{90}{-15} =$

   A. -10

   (B.) -6

   C. 1

   D. 10

10. $1\frac{1}{2} \div \frac{5}{6} =$

   A. $1\frac{4}{5}$

   B. $1\frac{1}{4}$

   C. $\frac{5}{9}$

   D. $\frac{5}{6}$

$$1\frac{1}{2} \div \frac{5}{6}$$
$$\frac{1}{2} \times \frac{6}{5} = 1\frac{6}{10} =$$

11. $(-5)(\frac{3}{10}) =$

    A. $-17\frac{1}{3}$

    (B) $-1\frac{1}{2}$

    C. $-\frac{4}{5}$

    D. $-\frac{3}{5}$

$\frac{5}{1} \times \frac{3}{10} = \frac{-15}{10}$

$-1\frac{5}{10} = -1\frac{1}{2}$

12. $-1\frac{1}{4} \div -1\frac{3}{4} =$

    A. $\frac{5}{7}$

    B. $\frac{9}{11}$

    C. $1\frac{2}{5}$

    (D) $2\frac{3}{16}$

$-1\frac{1}{4} \div -1\frac{3}{4}$

$-1\frac{1}{4} \times -1\frac{3}{4} = 2\frac{3}{16}$

13. $(-6)(-1\frac{2}{3}) =$

    A. -10

    B. $-3\frac{3}{5}$

    C. $3\frac{3}{5}$

    D. 10

$\frac{-6}{1} \times -1\frac{2}{3} = -1\frac{12}{3}$

14. $\frac{1}{2} \div -2 =$

    A. -4

    (B) -2

    C. -1

    D. $-\frac{1}{4}$

$\frac{1}{2} \div -\frac{2}{1} =$

$\frac{1}{2} \times -\frac{2}{1} = \left(\frac{2}{2}\right)$

15. $-1 \div -1\frac{2}{3} =$

    (A) $-1\frac{2}{3}$

    B. $-\frac{3}{5}$

    C. $\frac{3}{5}$

    D. $1\frac{2}{3}$

$\frac{-1}{1} \div -1\frac{2}{3}$

$\frac{-1}{1} \times -1\frac{3}{2} = -1\frac{3}{2}$

16. $2\frac{1}{5} \times 1\frac{1}{4} =$

    A. $\frac{25}{44}$

    B. $1\frac{19}{25}$

    C. 2

    D. $2\frac{3}{4}$

$2\frac{1}{20}$

17. $-9 \times 0 =$

    A. -9

    B. $-\frac{1}{9}$

    (C) 0

    D. undefined

18. $\frac{-7}{2} =$

    A. -14

    B. -9

    C. -5

    (D) -3.5

19. $-30 \div 2.5 =$

    A. -75

    B. -32.5

    C. -27.5

    (D) -12

20. $\frac{-6}{0} =$

    A. -6

    B. -1

    (C) 0

    D. undefined

Lesson 3: Multiplying and Dividing Rational Numbers

Converting Fractions, Decimals, and Percents

LESSON 4

You will learn how to:

• convert fractions to decimals

• convert fractions to percents

• compute and estimate with percents

Key Word: percent

Mark made 11 of the 20 shots he attempted in a basketball game. Mark wanted to know what percent of his attempts he made. His coach told him that he needed to convert a fraction to a decimal, then a decimal to a percent. Mark knew that he made $\frac{11}{20}$ of the shots he attempted.

One way to convert a fraction to a decimal is to find an equivalent fraction with a denominator of 100. Then write the equivalent fraction as a decimal.

$$\overset{\times 5}{\overset{\frown}{\frac{11}{20}}} = \frac{55}{100} = .55$$
$$\underset{\times 5}{\underset{\smile}{}}$$

The fraction $\frac{55}{100}$ and the decimal 0.55 represent the same number. They are both read "fifty-five hundredths." *Percent* means "per hundred," or "hundredths," so you can rename the number "fifty-five percent." Using the symbol % for percent, you can write $\frac{55}{100} = 0.55 = 55\%$.

Mark made 55% of his attempts.

To convert a decimal to a percent, move the decimal point two places to the right and add a percent symbol.

$$0.\underset{\smile}{55} = 55\%$$

Another way to convert a fraction to a decimal is to use division. This method is needed if 100 is not a multiple of the denominator, and it can be used with any fraction.

Example: Write $\frac{5}{8}$ as a decimal, then as a percent.

Divide to get a decimal, then convert to a percent.

$$8\overline{)5.000} \quad \begin{array}{c} 0.625 \end{array} \qquad 0.625 = 62.5\%$$

To divide monomials, divide the coefficients, then divide the variables. To divide a polynomial by a monomial, divide each term of the polynomial by the monomial.

Examples: Simplify using the rules of division and exponents.

$$\frac{(6rt^2)}{(-2t)} = \left(\frac{6}{-2}\right)\left(\frac{r}{1}\right)\left(\frac{t^2}{t}\right)$$
$$= (-3)(r)(t^{2-1})$$
$$= (-3)(r)(t)$$
$$= -3rt$$

$$\frac{x^2y}{2xy^3z} = \left(\frac{1}{2}\right)\left(\frac{x^2}{x}\right)\left(\frac{y}{y^3}\right)\left(\frac{1}{z}\right)$$
$$= \left(\frac{1}{2}\right)(x^{2-1})(y^{1-3})\left(\frac{1}{z}\right)$$
$$= \left(\frac{1}{2}\right)(x^1)(y^{-2})\left(\frac{1}{z}\right)$$
$$= \left(\frac{1}{2}\right)\left(\frac{x}{1}\right)\left(\frac{1}{y^2}\right)\left(\frac{1}{z}\right)$$
$$= \frac{x}{2y^2z}$$

$$\frac{9x^2 + 6x}{3x} = \frac{9x^2}{3x} + \frac{6x}{3x}$$
$$= \left(\frac{9}{3}\right)\left(\frac{x^2}{x}\right) + \left(\frac{6}{3}\right)\left(\frac{x}{x}\right)$$
$$= (3)(x^{2-1}) + (2)(1)$$
$$= (3)(x) + 2$$
$$= 3x + 2$$

Operations with polynomials can be used to solve word problems.

Examples:

Find an expression that represents the area of the rectangle.

$A = x(x - 4)$ To solve this problem, use the formula:
    $= x^2 - 4x$ Area = (length)(width).

The area is represented by the expression $x^2 - 4x$.

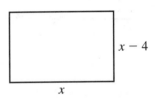

Find an expression that represents the area of the shaded region.

$A = (x + 4)(x) - (x + 1)(x - 3)$
$\quad = x^2 + 4x - [x^2 - 3x + 1x - 3]$
$\quad = x^2 + 4x - x^2 + 3x - x + 3$
$\quad = 6x + 3$

The area of the shaded region is represented by the expression $6x + 3$.

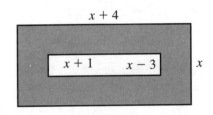

To solve this problem, use the formula: Area = (length)(width). Subtract the area of the smaller rectangle from the area of the larger one.

Self-Test

Circle the letter of the correct answer.

$2x(4x - 5) - 3(4x + 2) =$

A. $x^2 - 16$ C. $x - 16$

B. $8x^2 - 22x - 6$ D. $-4x^2 - 10x - 11$

Check your answer.

B is correct.

$2x(4x - 5) - 3(4x + 2)$

$= 2x(4x) + 2x(-5) - 3(4x) - 3(2)$

$= 8x^2 - 10x - 12x - 6$

$= 8x^2 - 22x - 6$

Practice

Multiplying and Dividing Monomials and Polynomials

Circle the letter of the correct answer.

1. $\frac{12w}{3} =$

   A. 4

   (B.) $4w$

   C. $6w$

   D. $9w$

2. $3(4y^2 + 2y) =$

   A. $12y^2$

   B. $12y^2 + 2y$

   (C.) $12y^2 + 6y$

   D. $18y^2$

3. $\frac{-6x^2}{12x} =$

   A. -2

   (B.) $-2x$

   C. $-\frac{x}{2}$

   D. $-2x^3$

4. $(2bc)(3bc) =$

   A. $5bc$

   B. $6bc$

   (C.) $6b^2c^2$

   D. $6b^3c^3$

5. $\frac{2x^2 + 6x - 4}{2} =$

   A. $x^2 - 3x - 2$

   (B.) $x^2 + 3x - 2$

   C. $x^2 + 3x + 2$

   D. $4x^2 - 2$

6. $(4mp^2)(-2m) =$

   (A.) $-8mp^2$

   B. $-8m^2p$

   C. $-8m^2p^2$

   D. $-8m^2p^3$

7. The length of the rectangle below is $2y + 1$. If the width is $3y$, find the area.

   A. $6y^2 - 1$

   B. $6y^2 + 3y$

   (C.) $6y^2 + 3y + 1$

   D. $6y^2 + 12y + 1$

8. The length of the rectangle below is 8 units longer than its width. Find the area.

   (A.) $w^2 + 8w$

   B. $w^2 - 64w$

   C. $w^2 + 8w + 8$

   D. $w^2 + 16w + 64$

9. $(x + 2)(x + 3) =$

   (A.) $x^2 + 5x$

   B. $x^2 + 5x - 6$

   C. $x^2 + 5x + 6$

   D. $x^2 + 5x + 36$

10. $\frac{5x^3 + 10x}{5x} =$

   A. $x^2 - 2$

   (B.) $x^2 + 2$

   C. $x^2 + 10$

   D. $5x^2 + 2$

11. One side of the square shown below is $4x$ units long. Find the area.

$4x$

A. $8x$

B. $16x$

C. $8x^2$

D. $16x^2$

12. $-4m(3m + 2) =$

A. $-20m$

B. $-12m^2 - 8m$

C. $-12m^2 + 2m$

D. $-12m^2 + 8m$

13. $(7a^2b^2)(6a^2b^3) =$

A. $42a^2b^6$

B. $42a^3b^6$

C. $42a^4b^5$

D. $42a^4b^6$

14. The two rectangles below have the dimensions shown. Which of the following represents the area of the shaded region?

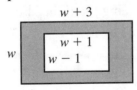

$w + 3$

$w + 1$

$w - 1$

w

A. $3w - 1$

B. $3w + 1$

C. $w^2 + 4w - 3$

D. $w^2 + 4w + 3$

15. $\frac{3n^3 + 6n^2 - 9n}{3n} =$

A. $n^2 + 2n - 3$

B. $n^2 + 6n - 9$

C. $3n^3 - 7n$

D. $3n^3 + 6n^2 - 3$

16. $(2n + 1)(n - 1) =$

A. $2n^2 - 1$

B. $2n^2 - n - 1$

C. $2n^2 + n - 1$

D. $2n^2 + n + 1$

17. The two rectangles below have the dimensions shown. Which of the following represents the area of the shaded region?

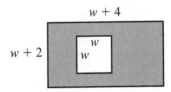

$w + 4$

w

w

$w + 2$

A. $6w + 8$

B. $6w^2 + 8$

C. $w^2 + 4w$

D. $w^2 + 6w + 8$

18. $(5x^2z)(-2xz^3) =$

A. $-10x^2z$

B. $-10x^2z^2$

C. $-10x^3z^3$

D. $-10x^3z^4$

19. $\frac{20nt^2}{-40n^3t} =$

A. $\frac{t^2}{-2n}$

B. $\frac{t}{-2n}$

C. $\frac{t}{-2n^2}$

D. $\frac{-2t}{n^2}$

20. $(m^2 + 2)(m^2 - 6) =$

A. $m^2 - 4m - 12$

B. $m^2 - 4m + 12$

C. $m^4 - 4m^2 - 12$

D. $m^4 - 4m^2 + 12$

Solving Two-Step Linear Equations

L E S S O N   1 7

You will learn how to:
- solve two-step linear equations in one variable
- check solutions to two-step linear equations

Key Words: linear equation, solution

A *linear equation* is an equation with one or more variables, each of which is raised to the first power.

Examples: $2 + n = 5$ $3r = 30$ $3x + 2y = 12$

In this lesson you will solve linear equations with one variable.

A *solution* to a linear equation with one variable is a number that makes the equation true.

Examples:

Equations: $2 + n = 5$ $3r = 30$
Solutions: $n = 3$ $r = 10$

To find a solution, isolate the variable, or get it by itself on one side of the equation.

If the variable is part of an expression, undo any indicated operations in that expression.

Examples:

expression:	$2 + n$	$3r$
indicated operation:	2 and n are being added	r is being multiplied by 3
to undo it:	subtract 2	divide by 3

If you perform an operation on one side of an equation, be sure to perform the same operation on the other side of that equation.

Check your solution by substituting it into the original equation. If the solution makes the equation true, then it is correct.

Examples:

$2 + n = 5$

$2 + n - \mathbf{2} = 5 - \mathbf{2}$

$(2 - 2) + n = 5 - 2$

$n = 3$

Check.
$2 + n = 5$
$2 + (3) \overset{?}{=} 5$
$5 = 5$

$3r = 30$

$\dfrac{3r}{3} = \dfrac{30}{3}$

$\left(\dfrac{3}{3}\right)(r) = \dfrac{30}{3}$

$r = 10$

Check.
$3r = 30$
$3(10) \overset{?}{=} 30$
$30 = 30$

Example: Solve $-2x \le 4$ for x.

$-2x \le 4$

$\dfrac{-2x}{-2} \ge \dfrac{4}{-2}$ ← Reverse the inequality symbol, because

$x \ge -2$ you are dividing by a negative number.

Check. Use $x = 0$.

$-2x \le 4$

$2(0) \overset{?}{\le} 4$

$0 \le 4$

Now try some two-step inequalities.

Examples: Solve $2y + 6 > 14$ for y.

$2y + 6 > 14$

$2y + 6 - 6 > 14 - 6$

$2y > 8$ ← The inequality symbol stays the

$\dfrac{2y}{2} > \dfrac{8}{2}$ same, because the 2 is positive.

$y > 4$

Check. Use $y = 5$.

$2y + 6 > 5$

$2(5) + 6 \overset{?}{>} 14$

$10 + 6 \overset{?}{>} 14$

$16 > 14$

Solve $-2w - 5 \ge 9$ for w.

$-2w - 5 \ge 9$

$-2w - 5 + 5 \ge 9 + 5$ ← Reverse the inequality symbol,

$-2w \ge 14$ because you are dividing by a

$\dfrac{-2w}{-2} \le \dfrac{14}{-2}$ negative number.

$w \le -7$

Check. Use $w = -8$.

$-2w - 5 \ge 9$

$-2(-8) - 5 \overset{?}{\ge} 9$

$16 - 5 \overset{?}{\ge} 9$

$11 \ge 9$

Self-Test

Circle the letter of the correct answer.

Solve $-4n + 2 \le -10$ for n.

A. $n \le 3$ C. $n \le 2$

B. $n \ge 3$ D. $n \ge 2$

Check your answer.

B is correct.

$-4n + 2 \le -10$

$-4n + 2 - 2 \le -10 - 2$

$-4n \le -12$

$\dfrac{-4n}{-4} \ge \dfrac{-12}{-4}$

$n \ge 3$

Check. *Use* $n = 4$.

$-4n + 2 \le -10$

$-4(4) + 2 \overset{?}{\le} -10$

$-16 + 2 \overset{?}{\le} -10$

$-14 \le -10$

Practice

Solving Two-Step Linear Inequalities

Circle the letter of the correct answer.

1. Solve $x - 2 < 3$ for x.

   A. $x < 1$
   B. $x > 1$
   C. $x < 5$
   D. $x > 5$

2. Solve $4y \leq 12$ for y.

   A. $y \geq 3$
   B. $y \leq 3$
   C. $y \geq 8$
   D. $y \leq 8$

3. Solve $2n + 3 > 7$ for n.

   A. $n > \frac{7}{5}$
   B. $n < \frac{7}{5}$
   C. $n > 2$
   D. $n < 2$

4. Solve $5r - 6 < 14$ for r.

   A. $r > \frac{8}{5}$
   B. $r < 4$
   C. $r > 4$
   D. $r < 15$

5. Solve $3l - 6 \geq -6$ for l.

   A. $l \geq -4$
   B. $l \leq -4$
   C. $l \geq 0$
   D. $l \leq 0$

6. Solve $7t - 8 \leq 13$ for t.

   A. $t \geq \frac{5}{7}$
   B. $t \leq \frac{5}{7}$
   C. $t \geq 3$
   D. $t \leq 3$

7. Solve $2q + 10 < -12$ for q.

   A. $q < -11$
   B. $q > -11$
   C. $q < -1$
   D. $q > -1$

8. Solve $12p - 19 > 5$ for p.

   A. $p > -\frac{5}{7}$
   B. $p < 0$
   C. $p > 2$
   D. $p < \frac{7}{2}$

9. Solve $-6m + 3 \geq -15$ for m.

   A. $m \leq -3$
   B. $m \geq -2$
   C. $m \leq 2$
   D. $m \leq 3$

10. Solve $5b + 12 > -13$ for b.

   A. $b > -5$
   B. $b < -\frac{13}{17}$
   C. $b > -\frac{1}{5}$
   D. $b < 5$

Lesson 19: Solving Two-Step Linear Inequalities

11. Solve $2q + 7 < -19$ for q.

    A. $q < -13$

    B. $q > -6$

    C. $q < -\frac{19}{9}$

    D. $q > -2$

12. Solve $-3n + 2 \leq -7$ for n.

    A. $n \leq -7$

    B. $n \geq -3$

    C. $n \leq \frac{5}{3}$

    D. $n \geq 3$

13. Solve $8b + 5 < 21$ for b.

    A. $b < 1$

    B. $b > \frac{21}{13}$

    C. $b < 2$

    D. $b > \frac{13}{4}$

14. Solve $-3y + 12 \geq -12$ for y.

    A. $y \geq -8$

    B. $y \leq -\frac{4}{3}$

    C. $y \leq 0$

    D. $y \leq 8$

15. Solve $6r + 7 \geq 7$ for r.

    A. $r \geq 0$

    B. $r \leq \frac{7}{13}$

    C. $r \geq \frac{7}{3}$

    D. $r \leq 6$

16. Solve $15c - 37 \geq 23$ for c.

    A. $c \geq -\frac{14}{15}$

    B. $c \geq 4$

    C. $c \leq 12$

    D. $c \leq 45$

17. Solve $7x + 12 \leq -16$ for x.

    A. $x \leq -4$

    B. $x \geq -2$

    C. $x \leq -\frac{4}{7}$

    D. $x \geq -\frac{16}{19}$

18. Solve $-9n - 17 > 13$ for n.

    A. $n > -3$

    B. $n < -\frac{10}{3}$

    C. $n > \frac{4}{9}$

    D. $n < \frac{1}{2}$

19. Solve $-4p + 11 \geq -21$ for p.

    A. $p \geq -3$

    B. $p \leq \frac{5}{2}$

    C. $p \leq 7$

    D. $p \leq 8$

20. Solve $8t - 31 < 25$ for t.

    A. $t < -\frac{25}{23}$

    B. $t > -\frac{3}{4}$

    C. $t < 7$

    D. $t > 8$

Solving Multi-Step Linear Inequalities

LESSON 20

You will learn how to:
- solve multi-step linear inequalities in one variable
- check solutions to multi-step linear inequalities

The steps used to solve a multi-step linear inequality are similar to the steps used to solve a multi-step linear equation. However, it is important to remember that if you multiply or divide both sides of an inequality by a negative number, you need to reverse the direction of the inequality symbol. To check your solution set, choose a number from the solution set to substitute into the original inequality. If you choose the boundary value to check, be sure to check another number from the solution set.

If like terms appear on the same side of an inequality, combine them.

Example: Solve $3h + 4 - h + 2 \geq 10$ for h.

$$3h + 4 - h + 2 \geq 10$$
$$(3h - h) + 4 + 2 \geq 10 \qquad \leftarrow \text{Combine like terms.}$$
$$2h + 6 \geq 10$$
$$2h \geq 4$$
$$h \geq 2$$

Check. Use $h = 3$.
$$3h + 4 - h + 2 \geq 10$$
$$3(3) + 4 - (3) + 2 \overset{?}{\geq} 10$$
$$9 + 4 - 3 + 2 \overset{?}{\geq} 10$$
$$13 - 3 + 2 \overset{?}{\geq} 10$$
$$10 + 2 \overset{?}{\geq} 10$$
$$12 \geq 10$$

If both sides of an inequality contain a variable term, add or subtract as needed to isolate the variable on one side.

Example: Solve $3w + 6 > 12 + 5w$ for w.

$$3w + 6 > 12 + 5w$$
$$3w - 5w + 6 > 12 + 5w - 5w \qquad \leftarrow \text{Subtract } 5w \text{ from both sides.}$$
$$-2w + 6 > 12$$
$$-2w > 6$$
$$w < -3$$

Check. Use $w = -4$.
$$3w + 6 > 12 + 5w$$
$$3(-4) + 6 \overset{?}{>} 12 + 5(-4)$$
$$-12 + 6 \overset{?}{>} 12 - 20$$
$$-6 > -8$$

If the inequality contains parentheses, distribute to remove them.
To distribute, multiply the polynomial by the monomial.

Example: Solve $-1(9x + 5) + 2(x - 2) \geq -30$ for x.

$$-1(9x + 5) + 2(x - 2) \geq -30$$
$$-1(9x) - 1(5) + 2(x) + 2(-2) \geq -30 \qquad \leftarrow \text{Distribute}$$
$$-9x - 5 + 2x - 4 \geq -30 \qquad \qquad -1 \text{ and } 2.$$
$$(-9x + 2x) + (-5 - 4) \geq -30 \qquad \leftarrow \text{Combine}$$
$$-7x - 9 \geq -30 \qquad \qquad \text{like terms.}$$
$$-7x \geq -21$$
$$x \leq 3$$

Check. Use $x = 2$.
$-1(9x + 5) + 2(x - 2) \geq -30$
$-1(9(2) + 5) + 2((2) - 2) \overset{?}{\geq} -30$
$-1(18 + 5) + 2(0) \overset{?}{\geq} -30$
$-1(23) + 0 \overset{?}{\geq} -30$
$-23 \geq -30$

Self-Test
Circle the letter of the correct answer.

1. Solve $4x - 5 + 6x + 20 \leq 0$ for x.

  A. $x \leq -\frac{3}{2}$ C. $x \leq -5$

  B. $x \geq -\frac{3}{2}$ D. $x \geq 5$

2. Solve $3(m - 3) - 5(m - 1) > 8$ for m.

  A. $m < -\frac{5}{8}$ C. $m < -6$

  B. $m < -5$ D. $m < -8$

Check your answer.

1. *A is correct.*

$$4x - 5 + 6x + 20 \leq 0$$
$$(4x + 6x) + (-5 + 20) \leq 0$$
$$10x + 15 \leq 0$$
$$10x \leq -15$$
$$x \leq -\frac{3}{2}$$

2. *C is correct.*

$$3(m - 3) - 5(m - 1) > 8$$
$$3m + 3(-3) - 5m - 5(-1) > 8$$
$$3m - 9 - 5m + 5 > 8$$
$$(3m - 5m) + (-9 + 5) > 8$$
$$-2m - 4 > 8$$
$$-2m > 12$$
$$m < -6$$

Practice

Solving Multi-Step Linear Inequalities

Circle the letter of the correct answer.

1. Solve $3x + 7 < 2x - 7$ for x.

   A. $x < -14$

   B. $x < -7$

   C. $x > 0$

   D. $x > 2$

2. Solve $3(x - 1) < 5$ for x.

   A. $x < \frac{2}{3}$

   B. $x < \frac{8}{3}$

   C. $x < 3$

   D. $x < 5$

3. Solve $2(y + 2) - 6(1 - y) \geq 2$ for y.

   A. $y \geq -1$

   B. $y \geq \frac{1}{2}$

   C. $y \geq 2$

   D. $y \geq 6$

4. Solve $3n - 2 \leq 5n$ for n.

   A. $n \leq -2$

   B. $n \geq -1$

   C. $n \geq 1$

   D. $n \leq 1$

5. Solve $7t - 8 \geq 13$ for t.

   A. $t > \frac{5}{3}$

   B. $t \leq 3$

   C. $t \geq 3$

   D. $t < 3$

6. Solve $3(6r + 1) - (12r - 5) \geq 0$ for r.

   A. $r \geq -\frac{4}{3}$

   B. $r \geq -1$

   C. $r \geq 0$

   D. $r \geq \frac{2}{3}$

7. Solve $5b - 2 - (2b + 3) \leq b$ for b.

   A. $b \leq -\frac{1}{2}$

   B. $b \leq \frac{5}{3}$

   C. $b \leq \frac{5}{2}$

   D. $b \leq 5$

8. Solve $-3c + 4 - (5 - 6c) < 5$ for c.

   A. $c < -\frac{2}{3}$

   B. $c < 2$

   C. $c < 3$

   D. $c < 4$

9. Solve $7w - 3 - 4(3w + 10) > 2$ for w.

   A. $w < -9$

   B. $w > -9$

   C. $w < -7$

   D. $w > -7$

10. Solve $10 - 5(2z + 1) \leq 2z - 7$ for z.

    A. $z \leq -1$

    B. $z \geq 1$

    C. $z \geq \frac{3}{2}$

    D. $z \leq 2$

11. Solve $8(b + 1) - (b - 4) < 3b$ for b.

A. $b < -3$

B. $b > -3$

C. $b < -1$

D. $b < \frac{3}{4}$

12. Solve $3a + 1 > 4(2a - 1)$ for a.

A. $a < 0$

B. $a < \frac{2}{5}$

C. $a < 1$

D. $a > 2$

13. Solve $-2(3d - 4) \leq d + 7$ for d.

A. $d \leq \frac{1}{7}$

B. $d \geq \frac{1}{7}$

C. $d \leq 3$

D. $d \geq 3$

14. Solve $6c + 8 > 2(c + 8)$ for c.

A. $c < 0$

B. $c < 2$

C. $c > 2$

D. $c > 4$

15. Solve $3(y + 11) - 2(y + 10) \leq 4y + 1$ for y.

A. $y \geq 2$

B. $y \geq 4$

C. $y \leq \frac{20}{3}$

D. $y \leq \frac{52}{3}$

16. Solve $5(2z - 1) - (z + 2) < 0$ for z.

A. $z < -\frac{1}{9}$

B. $z < \frac{9}{7}$

C. $z < \frac{1}{3}$

D. $z < \frac{7}{9}$

17. Solve $4n - 7 \geq 5(2n + 7)$ for n.

A. $n \leq -7$

B. $n \leq -5$

C. $n \leq -\frac{7}{3}$

D. $n \leq 0$

18. Solve $3x + 5 \leq 7x + 8$ for x.

A. $x \leq -\frac{4}{3}$

B. $x \geq -\frac{4}{3}$

C. $x \geq -\frac{3}{4}$

D. $x \leq -\frac{3}{4}$

19. Solve $5p + 7 - 2(p - 5) < 2$ for p.

A. $p < -5$

B. $p > -\frac{10}{3}$

C. $p < 0$

D. $p > \frac{5}{3}$

20. Solve $7(t + 8) - 6(t + 9) \geq 2$ for t.

A. $t \geq -15$

B. $t \geq -2$

C. $t \geq 0$

D. $t \geq 3$

Solving Word Problems with Equations and Inequalities

LESSON 21

You will learn how to:
- solve word problems using equations and inequalities

Key Word: translate

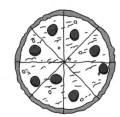

Example:

Ruth and four friends want pizza. If they each plan to eat
3 slices and there are 8 slices per pizza, how many pizzas
should they order to make sure there is enough?

Represent the unknown with a variable.   → Let p = the number of pizzas the group of
friends should order.

**Identify the given information and any
related facts.**   → There are 5 people, including Ruth.
Each person plans to eat 3 slices.
There are 8 slices per pizza.

State the requirement that must be satisfied.   → The number of slices ordered must be at
least as many as the number of slices they
plan to eat.

Translate the requirement into an equation or inequality.

The number of slices ordered must be at least as many as the number of slices they plan to eat.

$$8p \qquad\qquad \geq \qquad\qquad 15$$

They will order p pizzas, and | "at least as many as" | There are 5 people, and each plans
each pizza has 8 slices, so | means | to eat 3 slices, so they plan to eat
there will be $8p$ slices. | "greater than or equal to" | $(5)(3)$, or 15 slices.

Solve the inequality.   → $8p \geq 15$

$$\frac{8p}{8} \geq \frac{15}{8}$$

$$p \geq \frac{15}{8}$$

$$p \geq 1\frac{7}{8}$$

Answer the question.   → The group of friends should order 2 pizzas to be sure
Be sure your answer   they have enough.
makes sense.

Example: A school basketball team sells programs for $1.50 before each game. The team pays $110 plus $0.30 per program for the programs. How many programs must the team sell to make a profit of $250?

Represent the unknown with a variable.   → Let p = the number of programs.

Identify the given information and any related facts.

→ Amount earned = $1.50p$
Amount spent = $110 + $0.30p$
Profit = $1.50p - (110 + 0.30p)$

State the requirement that must be satisfied.   → The team wants the profit to be $250.

Translate the requirement into an equation.

Solve the equation.

→ $1.50p - (110 + 0.30p) = 250$
$$1.50p - 110 - 0.30p = 250$$
$$1.20p - 110 = 250$$
$$1.20p = 360$$
$$p = 300$$

Answer the question.   → The team must sell 300 programs to make a $250 profit.

Self-Test

Circle the letter of the correct answer.

1. Jim has $20 and his sister has $95. If Jim saves $5 each week and his sister spends $10 each week, how many weeks will it be before Jim and his sister have the same amount?

   A. 5 weeks   C. 9 weeks

   B. 7 weeks   D. 11 weeks

2. A store charges $4 per game to rent a video game. A club charges only $2 per game, but has a membership fee of $50 per year. At least how many games must you rent each year so that renting from the club costs less than renting from the store?

   A. 24 games   C. 26 games

   B. 25 games   D. 35 games

Check your answer.

A is correct.

w = the number of weeks
Jim's money = 20 + 5w
His sister's money = 95 − 10w

20 + 5w = 95 − 10w
*   w = 5*

B is correct.

Let g = the number of games.
Cost to rent from the store = 4g
Cost to rent from the club = 2g + 50
You want the club cost to be less than the store cost.

2g + 50 < 4g
*   g > 25*

Practice

Solving Word Problems with Equations and Inequalities

Circle the letter of the correct answer.

1. Grace has twice as much money as Tad. Together they have $36. How much money does Tad have?

    A. $4
    B. $6
    C. $12
    D. $18

2. The 10th grade class has 17 more girls than boys. If there are 431 students in the 10th grade, how many of those students are boys?

    A. 200 boys
    B. 207 boys
    C. 224 boys
    D. 253 boys

3. A city is hosting a local pet show. There are 110 cats, dogs, and hamsters in the show. If there are twice as many dogs as cats and ten fewer hamsters than cats, how many cats are in the show?

    A. 20 cats
    B. 25 cats
    C. 30 cats
    D. 40 cats

4. Kate has $4 more than twice as much money as Joe does. Joe has $16 less than Marcia does. In all they have $220. How much money does Joe have?

    A. $40
    B. $50
    C. $60
    D. $80

5. A manufacturer of remote-control race cars sells them for $18 each. The cost to run the company is $2,000 per day plus $13 to build each car. What is the minimum number of cars that must be sold each day for the company to make a profit?

    A. 351 cars
    B. 401 cars
    C. 426 cars
    D. 476 cars

6. The school band bought 1,000 boxes of candy for $250. What price per box must the band charge to make a $500 profit?

    A. $0.25
    B. $0.50
    C. $0.75
    D. $1.00

7. A chef wants to bake a 3-pound chicken. She has at most 105 minutes to prepare and bake the chicken. If she spends 45 minutes preparing the chicken, how many minutes per pound will be allowed for baking it?

    A. 17 minutes
    B. 18 minutes
    C. 19 minutes
    D. 20 minutes

8. A jury has 12 members. There are 4 more women than men. How many men are on the jury?

    A. 3 men
    B. 4 men
    C. 5 men
    D. 8 men

9. Melanie is 2 years older than her brother Tim. Ryan is 5 years younger than Melanie. If the sum of their ages is 56, how old is Melanie?

    A. 17 years old

    B. 19 years old

    C. 21 years old

    D. 23 years old

10. A new swimming pool charges $3 per day, or $1 with an $80 membership fee. How many times must you go swimming to save money with the membership?

    A. at least 11 times

    B. at least 21 times

    C. at least 31 times

    D. at least 41 times

11. A family drove 200 miles in all. They stopped along the way to have lunch. If the distance the family traveled after they stopped was 3 times the distance they traveled before they stopped, how many miles did the family drive before they stopped?

    A. 50 miles

    B. 75 miles

    C. 100 miles

    D. 125 miles

12. Jeff has $250 and Tina has $125. If Jeff saves $20 per month, and Tina saves $45 per month, how many months will it be before they have the same amount?

    A. 2 months

    B. 3 months

    C. 4 months

    D. 5 months

13. A sweet shop makes half as much money on ice cream as on chocolate. If the store makes $375, how much of that is from chocolate sales?

    A. $100

    B. $125

    C. $250

    D. $300

14. A local group was charged $2,500 plus $2 per CD to press 500 copies of their first CD. For how much must they sell each CD in order to make $4,500?

    A. $10

    B. $12

    C. $14

    D. $16

15. Ivana and Gloria are sisters. Gloria is 35 years old. Three years ago Gloria was four times as old as Ivana. How old is Ivana now?

    A. 11 years old

    B. 12 years old

    C. 13 years old

    D. 14 years old

16. An empty 60-gallon tank is being filled at a rate of 10 gallons per hour. A hole is letting water out at a rate of 4 gallons per hour. How long will it take to fill the tank?

    A. 6 hours

    B. 8 hours

    C. 10 hours

    D. 12 hours

Solving Absolute Value Equations

LESSON 22

You will learn how to:
• solve equations using absolute values

Key Words: absolute value equation

Recall that the absolute value of a number is that number's distance from zero on a number line.

A number and its opposite have the same absolute value. For example, $|6| = 6$ and $|-6| = 6$ because both 6 and -6 are 6 units from zero on a number line.

In the *absolute value equation* $|x| = 6$, x represents any number whose distance from zero on a number line is 6 units. The solution set for this equation is $\{6, -6\}$.

Example: Solve $|x| = 5$.

x represents any number whose distance from zero on a number line is 5 units. The solution set for this equation is $\{5, -5\}$.

Example: Solve $|x - 2| = 5$.

The expression $x - 2$ represents any number whose distance from zero on a number line is 5 units.

Write and solve two equations:

$$x - 2 = 5 \qquad \text{or} \qquad x - 2 = -5$$
$$x = 7 \qquad\qquad\qquad x = -3$$

The solution set is $\{-3, 7\}$.

Check your solutions.

Check 7.	Check -3.
$|x - 2| = 5$	$|x - 2| = 5$
$|7 - 2| \overset{?}{=} 5$	$|-3 - 2| \overset{?}{=} 5$
$|5| \overset{?}{=} 5$	$|-5| \overset{?}{=} 5$
$5 = 5$	$5 = 5$

Examples: Solve $|y + 3| = 4$.

$$y + 3 = 4 \quad \text{or} \quad y + 3 = -4$$
$$y = 1 \qquad\qquad\quad y = -7$$

The solution set is $\{-7, 1\}$.

Solve $|2z + 7| = 11$.

$$2z + 7 = 11 \quad \text{or} \quad 2z + 7 = -11$$
$$2z = 4 \qquad\qquad\quad 2z = -18$$
$$z = 2 \qquad\qquad\quad z = -9$$

The solution set is $\{2, -9\}$.

Solve $|8 - k| = 3$.

$$8 - k = 3 \quad \text{or} \quad 8 - k = -3$$
$$-k = -5 \qquad\qquad -k = -11$$
$$k = 5 \qquad\qquad\quad k = 11$$

The solution set is $\{5, 11\}$.

Solve $|1 - 2a| = 7$.

$$1 - 2a = 7 \quad \text{or} \quad 1 - 2a = -7$$
$$-2a = 6 \qquad\qquad -2a = -8$$
$$a = -3 \qquad\qquad\quad a = 4$$

The solution set is $\{-3, 4\}$.

Examples: Solve $|2r| + 2 = 10$.

Isolate the absolute value expression on one side of the equation, then write and solve two equations.

$$|2r| + 2 = 10$$
$$|2r| + 2 - 2 = 10 - 2$$
$$|2r| = 8$$
$$2r = 8 \quad \text{or} \quad 2r = -8$$
$$r = 4 \quad \text{or} \quad r = -4$$

The solution set is $\{4, -4\}$.

Examples: Solve $|x| = 0$.

Zero is the only number that has an absolute value of zero.

The solution set is $\{0\}$.

Example: Solve $|x + 3| = -5$.

This equation has no solution because an absolute value is never negative.

Solve $3 - 4|x| = -5$.

Isolate the absolute value expression on one side of the equation, then write and solve two equations.

$$3 - 4|x| = -5$$
$$3 - 4|x| - 3 = -5 - 3$$
$$-4|x| = -8$$
$$\frac{-4|x|}{-4} = \frac{-8}{-4}$$
$$|x| = 2$$
$$x = 2 \quad \text{or} \quad x = -2$$

The solution set is $\{2, -2\}$.

Solve $|3a + 6| = 0$.

$$3a + 6 = 0$$
$$3a = -6$$
$$a = -2$$

The solution set is $\{-2\}$.

Self-Test

Circle the letter of the correct answer.

1. Solve for n. $|n| = 10$

   A. $\{-10\}$ C. $\{10, -10\}$

   B. $\{10\}$ D. $\{0, 10\}$

2. The solution set for $|y + 5| = 3$ is

   A. $\{-2, -8\}$ C. $\{-2, 2\}$

   B. $\{-2, 8\}$ D. $\{-8, 8\}$

Check your answer.

1. *C is correct.*
   n represents any number whose distance from zero is 10 units. The two numbers are 10 and -10. The solution set is $\{10, -10\}$.

2. *A is correct.*
   $|y + 5| = 3$
   $y + 5 = 3 \quad \text{or} \quad y + 5 = -3$
   $y = -2 \qquad\qquad y = -8$
   The solution set is $\{-2, -8\}$.

© Pearson Education, Inc./Globe Fearon/Pearson Learning Group. All rights reserved. Copying strictly prohibited.

Lesson 22: Solving Absolute Value Equations   87

Practice

Solving Absolute Value Equations

Circle the letter of the correct answer.

1. Which of the following is the solution set of $|x| = 5$?

   A. $\{5, 0\}$

   B. $\{0, -5\}$

   C. $\{5\}$

   D. $\{-5, 5\}$

2. $\{7, -7\}$ is the solution set for which of the following equations?

   A. $|a| = -7$

   B. $|a| = 7$

   C. $|a| = 0$

   D. $|a| = 14$

3. Solve for a.
   $|1 - a| = 4$

   A. $\{3, -3\}$

   B. $\{5, -5\}$

   C. $\{-3, 5\}$

   D. $\{3, -5\}$

4. Which of the following is a solution of $|-3y| = 6$?

   A. -12

   B. -2

   C. 0

   D. $\frac{1}{2}$

5. Solve for a.
   $|a - 5| = 1$

   A. $\{4, -4\}$

   B. $\{6, -6\}$

   C. $\{6, 4\}$

   D. $\{-6, -4\}$

6. Which of the following is the solution set of $|n + 6| = 3$?

   A. $\{-3, -9\}$

   B. $\{-3, 9\}$

   C. $\{3, 9\}$

   D. $\{3, -9\}$

7. $|x| = 0$ has how many solutions?

   A. no solutions

   B. one solution

   C. two solutions

   D. an infinite number of solutions

8. Which of the following is a solution of $|4 - b| = 8$?

   A. -4

   B. -2

   C. 2

   D. 4

9. Which of the following is the solution set of $|6 - t| = 5$?

   A. $\{1\}$

   B. $\{1, -11\}$

   C. $\{-1, -11\}$

   D. $\{1, 11\}$

10. Solve for b.
    $|b + 9| = 0$

    A. $\{9, -9\}$

    B. $\{-9\}$

    C. $\{0\}$

    D. no solution

Lesson 22: Solving Absolute Value Equations

11. Which of the following is the solution set of $|1 - n| = 0$?

A. $\{-1\}$

B. $\{0\}$

C. $\{1\}$

D. $\{1, -1\}$

12. Solve for x.

$|2x + 3| = 1$

A. $\{-1, -2\}$

B. $\{-1, 2\}$

C. $\{1, -2\}$

D. $\{1, 2\}$

13. Solve the equation $|n| + 3 = 7$ for n.

A. $\{4, -10\}$

B. $\{4, -4\}$

C. $\{4, 10\}$

D. $\{-4, -10\}$

14. Solve for p.

$|p| - 5 = -2$

A. $\{3, -3\}$

B. $\{3, -7\}$

C. $\{3, 7\}$

D. no solution

15. Solve for x.

$4 - |2x| = -8$

A. $\{2, -2\}$

B. $\{-2, 6\}$

C. $\{6, -6\}$

D. no solution

16. Which of the following is a solution set of $|4x - 2| = 6$?

A. $\{-1, 2\}$

B. $\{1, 2\}$

C. $\{-2, -1\}$

D. $\{1, -2\}$

17. Which of the following is a solution of $|3x - 1| = 10$?

A. -4

B. -3

C. 3

D. 4

18. Which of the following is the solution set of $|-3x| = 12$?

A. $\{4\}$

B. $\{-4\}$

C. $\{-4, 4\}$

D. no solution

19. Solve for x.

$|6 - 2x| = 8$

A. $\{-1, 7\}$

B. $\{1, -7\}$

C. $\{-1, -7\}$

D. $\{1, 7\}$

20. Solve for n.

$|2n + 3| = -5$

A. $\{1, -1\}$

B. $\{-1, -4\}$

C. $\{-1, 4\}$

D. no solution

Lesson 22: Solving Absolute Value Equations

Solving Absolute Value Inequalities

LESSON 23

You will learn how to:
• solve inequalities involving absolute values

Key Words: absolute value inequality

In the absolute value equation $|n| = 3$, n represents any number that is 3 units from zero.

The solution set is $\{-3, 3\}$, and can be shown on a graph:

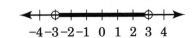

In the *absolute value inequality* $|n| < 3$, n represents any number that is less than 3 units from zero. There are an infinite number of values of n that are less than 3 units from 0, so there are an infinite number of solutions to this inequality.

The graph of this solution set is:

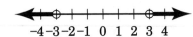

To write the inequality $|n| < 3$ without an absolute value symbol, write the compound inequality $n > -3$ and $n < 3$. The shorter version of this compound inequality is $-3 < n < 3$.

In the absolute value inequality $|n| > 3$, n represents any number that is more than 3 units from zero. There are also an infinite number of solutions to this inequality.

The graph of this solution set is:

This inequality can be written as $n < -3$ or $n > 3$. There is no shorter version for a compound inequality using *or* as the connecting word.

Examples:

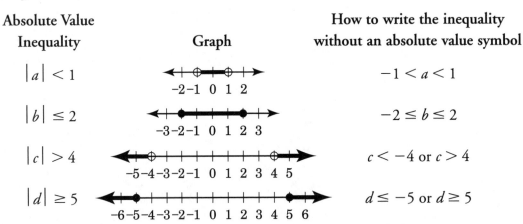

Absolute Value Inequality	Graph	How to write the inequality without an absolute value symbol
$|a| < 1$		$-1 < a < 1$
$|b| \leq 2$		$-2 \leq b \leq 2$
$|c| > 4$		$c < -4$ or $c > 4$
$|d| \geq 5$		$d \leq -5$ or $d \geq 5$

Lesson 23: Solving Absolute Value Inequalities

Example: Solve $|x - 17| \le 3$.

$$-3 \le \quad x - 17 \quad \le 3$$

Rewrite the inequality without the absolute value symbol.

$$14 \le \quad\quad x \quad\quad \le 20$$

Solve.

The solution set is given by: $14 \le x \le 20$.

Example: Assume y is an integer and solve for y.

$$|y + 2| < 3$$
$$-3 < y + 2 < 3$$
$$-5 < y < 1$$

Because y must be an integer, the solution set is $\{-4, -3, -2, -1, 0\}$.

Example: Solve $|2n - 5| > 1$.

$2n - 5 < -1$	or	$2n - 5 > 1$
$2n < 4$		$2n > 6$
$n < 2$		$n > 3$

Rewrite the inequality without the absolute value symbol. Solve each inequality.

The solution set is given by: $n < 2$ or $n > 3$.

Example: Assume z is an integer and solve for z. $15 - 2|z| > 7$.

$$15 - 2|z| - 15 > 7 - 15$$
$\leftarrow$ Subtract 15 from both sides of the inequality to isolate the absolute value term.

$$-2|z| > -8$$

$$\frac{-2|z|}{-2} < \frac{-8}{-2}$$
$\leftarrow$ Divide both sides by -2. Reverse the inequality sign.

$$|z| < 4$$

$$-4 < z < 4$$
$\leftarrow$ Rewrite without the absolute value symbol.

The solution set is $\{-3, -2, -1, 0, 1, 2, 3\}$.

Self-Test

Circle the letter of the correct answer.

1. Which is the graph of $|k| > 2$?

A. (number line graph) $-2\,-1\ 0\ 1\ 2$

C. (number line graph) $-2\,-1\ 0\ 1\ 2$

B. (number line graph) $-2\,-1\ 0\ 1\ 2$

D. (number line graph) $-2\,-1\ 0\ 1\ 2$

2. Assume n is an integer and solve for n.
$$|n - 3| \le 2$$

A. $\{1, 2, 3, 4, 5\}$

B. $\{-2, -1, 0, 1, 2\}$

C. $\{-5, -4, -3, -2, -1\}$

D. $\{2, 3, 4\}$

Check your answer.

1. *B is correct.*

   $|k| > 2$ means $k < -2$ or $k > 2$. The graph indicates this.

2. *A is correct.*

   $$|n - 3| \le 2$$
   $$-2 \le n - 3 \le 2$$
   $$1 \le n \le 5$$
   The solution set is $\{1, 2, 3, 4, 5\}$.

Lesson 23: Solving Absolute Value Inequalities

Practice

Solving Absolute Value Inequalities

Circle the letter of the correct answer.

1. Which is the graph of $|n| < 3$?

A. ![number line -3-2-1 0 1 2 3, open circles at -3 and 3]

B. ![number line -3-2-1 0 1 2 3, closed circles at -3 and 3]

C. ![number line -3-2-1 0 1 2 3, open circles at -3 and 3 with segment]

D. ![number line -3-2-1 0 1 2 3, closed circles at -3 and 3 with segment]

2. Solve $|y + 3| > 5$.

A. $y < -8$ or $y > 2$
B. $y \leq -8$ or $y \geq 2$
C. $-8 < y < 2$
D. $-8 \leq y \leq 2$

3. $|x| \leq 5$ has the same meaning as which of the following?

A. $x < -5$ or $x > 5$
B. $-5 < x < 5$
C. $x \leq -5$ or $x \geq 5$
D. $-5 \leq x \leq 5$

4. Which of the following is the set of all integers that satisfies $|a| < 4$?

A. $\{0, 1, 2, 3, 4\}$
B. $\{-3, -2, -1, 0, 1, 2, 3\}$
C. $\{-3, -2, -1, 0\}$
D. $\{-4, -3, -2, -1, 0, 1, 2, 3, 4\}$

5. $|b| > 1$ has the same meaning as which of the following?

A. $b < -1$ or $b > 1$
B. $b \leq -1$ or $b \geq 1$
C. $-1 < b < 1$
D. $-1 \leq b \leq 1$

6. Assume x is an integer and solve for x.
$|x - 1| < 4$

A. $\{-4, -3, -2, -1, 0, 1, 2\}$
B. $\{-3, -2, -1, 0, 1, 2, 3, 4\}$
C. $\{-2, -1, 0, 1, 2, 3, 4\}$
D. $\{-3, -2, -1, 0, 1, 2, 3, 4, 5\}$

7. What is the least integer in the solution set of $|b - 4| \leq 8$?

A. -4
B. -3
C. 11
D. 12

8. Which of the following inequalities has the solution set shown on the graph below?

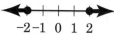

A. $|r| > 2$
B. $|r| \geq 2$
C. $|r| < 2$
D. $|r| \leq 2$

9. Assume that m is an integer and solve for m.
$|3 + m| < 2$

A. $\{-5, -4, -3, -2, -1, 0\}$
B. $\{0, 1, 2, 3, 4, 5\}$
C. $\{-4, -3, -2\}$
D. $\{-5, -4, -3, -2, -1\}$

10. Solve $|2z + 1| > 3$.

A. $-2 < z < 1$
B. $-2 \leq z \leq 1$
C. $z \leq -2$ or $z \geq 1$
D. $z < -2$ or $z > 1$

Lesson 23: Solving Absolute Value Inequalities

11. Assume p is an integer and solve for p.
$$|2p + 3| < 7$$
 A. $\{-5, -4, -3, -2, -1, 0, 1, 2\}$
 B. $\{-4, -3, -2, -1, 0, 1\}$
 C. $\{-6, -7, -8, \ldots\}$
 D. $\{3, 4, 5, \ldots\}$

12. Assume r is an integer and solve for r.
$$14 - 3|r| > 2$$
 A. $\{0, 1, 2, 3\}$
 B. $\{0, 1, 2, 3, 4\}$
 C. $\{-3, -2, -1, 0, 1, 2, 3\}$
 D. $\{-4, -3, -2, -1, 0, 1, 2, 3, 4\}$

13. Solve $|1 - x| > 5$.
 A. $x < -4$ or $x > 6$
 B. $x < -6$ or $x > 4$
 C. $-4 < x < 6$
 D. $-6 < x < 4$

14. Assume k is an integer and solve for k.
$$1 + 2|k| < 5$$
 A. $\{0, 1\}$
 B. $\{-1, 0, 1\}$
 C. $\{0, 1, 2\}$
 D. $\{-2, -1, 0, 1, 2\}$

15. Solve $3|n| - 2 \geq 1$.
 A. $n < -1$ or $n > 1$
 B. $n \leq -1$ or $n \geq 1$
 C. $-1 < n < 1$
 D. $-1 \leq n \leq 1$

16. What is the greatest integer in the solution set of $|2 - a| + 5 < 8$?
 A. -1
 B. 0
 C. 4
 D. 5

17. How many integers are in the solution set of $|w + 3| < 0$?
 A. 0
 B. 1
 C. 2
 D. 3

18. Assume h is an integer and solve for h.
$$7 - 2|h| \geq 5$$
 A. $\{-1, 0\}$
 B. $\{0, 1\}$
 C. $\{-1, 0, 1\}$
 D. $\{-1, 1\}$

19. Which of the following is a solution of $9 - |6 - s| < 8$?
 A. 5
 B. 6
 C. 7
 D. 8

20. Assume z is an integer and solve for z.
$$1 - 3|z| > -5$$
 A. $\{-2, -1, 0, 1, 2\}$
 B. $\{-1, 0, 1\}$
 C. $\{-2, 2\}$
 D. $\{0\}$

Lesson 23: Solving Absolute Value Inequalities

Verifying Solutions to Linear Equations and Graphing Linear Equations

LESSON 24

> You will learn how to:
> - verify a solution to a linear equation
> - make a table of values to graph a linear equation

> **Key Words:** linear equation in two variables, ordered pair, coordinate plane

Recall that a linear equation is an equation containing one or more variables, each of which is raised to the first power. A solution to a linear equation with only one variable is a number. For example, the solution to the equation $2x + 3 = 11$ is 4.

A solution to a *linear equation in two variables* is a pair of numbers. One solution to the equation $y = 2x + 3$ is the pair of numbers $x = 1$ and $y = 5$ because they make the equation true when they are substituted for the variables: $5 = 2(1) + 3$. This solution can be written as the ordered pair $(1, 5)$. In an *ordered pair*, the x-value is written first and the y-value is written second: (x, y).

Example: State whether each ordered pair is a solution of $y = 4x - 5$.

Ordered Pair	Substitution	Is it a solution?
	$y = 4x - 5$	
$(0, -5)$	$-5 \stackrel{?}{=} 4(0) - 5$ $-5 = -5$	Yes
$(-2, 3)$	$3 \stackrel{?}{=} 4(-2) - 5$ $3 \neq -13$	No
$(3, 7)$	$7 \stackrel{?}{=} 4(3) - 5$ $7 = 7$	Yes
$(1, -1)$	$-1 \stackrel{?}{=} 4(1) - 5$ $-1 = -1$	Yes

Notice that a linear equation in two variables has more than one solution. In fact, there are an infinite number of ordered pair solutions to any linear equation. If the solutions to a linear equation are graphed on a *coordinate plane*, they form a line, and every point on that line is a solution to that equation. The graph of $y = 4x - 5$ is shown at the right.

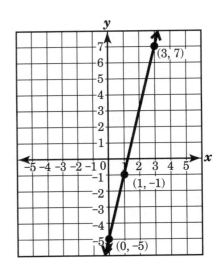

You can use a table of values to help you graph the solutions to a linear equation. One way to find solutions is to choose values to substitute for x, and then determine values for y to make the equation true. Choose at least 3 different values for x.

Example: Make a table of values to graph $2x + y = 3$.

Choose x-values	Determine the y-values	Ordered Pair
	$2x + y = 3$	
$x = -1$	$2(-1) + y = 3$ $-2 + y = 3$ $y = 5$	$(-1, 5)$
$x = 0$	$2(0) + y = 3$ $0 + y = 3$ $y = 3$	$(0, 3)$
$x = 1$	$2(1) + y = 3$ $2 + y = 3$ $y = 1$	$(1, 1)$

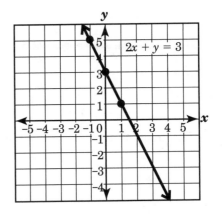

Self-Test
Circle the letter of the correct answer.

1. Which ordered pair is a solution of $x - y = 2$?

   A. (0, 2)   C. (2, 4)

   B. (1, 3)   D. (5, 3)

2. The ordered pair $(-2, 5)$ is a solution of which equation?

   A. $y = 3x - 1$ C. $y = 3x + 11$

   B. $y = 3x + 1$ D. $y = 3x - 11$

Check your answer.

1. *D is correct. Substitute 5 for x and 3 for y.*
   $x - y = 2$
   $5 - 3 \overset{?}{=} 2$
      $2 = 2$

2. *C is correct.*
   Substitute -2 for x and 5 for y.
   $y = 3x + 11$
   $5 \overset{?}{=} 3(-2) + 11$
   $5 = 5$

Practice

Verifying Solutions to Linear Equations and Graphing Linear Equations

Circle the letter of the correct answer.

1. Which ordered pair is a solution of $y = 2x - 5$?

   A. $(-1, -3)$
   B. $(1, 3)$
   C. $(-3, 1)$
   D. $(3, 1)$

2. Which of the following is a point on the graph of $x + y = -3$?

   A. $(-4, 1)$
   B. $(-3, -1)$
   C. $(0, 3)$
   D. $(3, 6)$

3. The graph of $4x + 2y = 8$ contains which point?

   A. $(1, 1)$
   B. $(1, 2)$
   C. $(2, 1)$
   D. $(3, -1)$

4. Which ordered pair is in the solution set of $6 - y = 2x$?

   A. $(0, 3)$
   B. $(0, -3)$
   C. $(-3, 0)$
   D. $(3, 0)$

5. Which ordered pair represents a point that does *not* lie on the graph of $y = -5x + 3$?

   A. $(1, -2)$
   B. $(0, 3)$
   C. $(-1, 8)$
   D. $(-3, 0)$

6. The graph of $x - 2y = 7$ does *not* contain which point?

   A. $(1, -3)$
   B. $(3, -2)$
   C. $(-1, 3)$
   D. $(5, -1)$

7. Which point does *not* lie on the line $3x - y = 8$?

   A. $(6, 10)$
   B. $(4, 4)$
   C. $(3, -1)$
   D. $(2, -2)$

8. Which ordered pair is *not* a solution of $2x + 3y = 12$?

   A. $(2, 3)$
   B. $(6, 0)$
   C. $(0, 4)$
   D. $(3, 2)$

9. The ordered pair $(-1, 3)$ is a solution of which equation?

   A. $y = 3x$
   B. $x + y = 2$
   C. $x - 3y = 0$
   D. $x - y = 2$

10. Which of these lines contains the point $(-2, -4)$?

   A. $y = x + 2$
   B. $y = x - 2$
   C. $2x + y = 8$
   D. $x + y = 6$

11. On which line does the point $(5, -1)$ lie?

 A. $x - y = 6$
 B. $x - y = 4$
 C. $x + y = 6$
 D. $x + y = -6$

12. The ordered pair $(1, 2)$ is a solution of which equation?

 A. $2x + y = 5$
 B. $x + 2y = 5$
 C. $3x - y = 5$
 D. $x - 3y = 5$

13. The ordered pair $(-1, -3)$ is *not* a solution of which equation?

 A. $y = 2x - 1$
 B. $y = x - 2$
 C. $x - y = 4$
 D. $x - 2y = 5$

14. The point $(0, 4)$ does *not* lie on which line?

 A. $y = 4x$
 B. $x + y = 4$
 C. $y = x + 4$
 D. $x + 2y = 8$

15. Which line does *not* contain the point $(3, 2)$?

 A. $3x + 2y = 13$
 B. $3x - 2y = 5$
 C. $2x + 3y = 12$
 D. $2x - 3y = -12$

16. If the x-value of a point on the line $3x + y = 2$ is -1, what is the corresponding value of y?

 A. 1
 B. 2
 C. 3
 D. 5

17. If the x-value of a point on the line $x + 2y = 9$ is -3, what is the corresponding value of y?

 A. -3
 B. 3
 C. 6
 D. 9

18. If the y-value of a point on the line $x - 2y = 1$ is 2, what is the corresponding value of x?

 A. 3
 B. 4
 C. 5
 D. 9

19. If the y-value of a point on the line $y = 3x - 1$ is -7, what is the corresponding value of x?

 A. -7
 B. -2
 C. 2
 D. 3

20. Which ordered pair is a solution of $y = -4x + 1$?

 A. $(1, -5)$
 B. $(1, -3)$
 C. $(-1, -3)$
 D. $(-1, -5)$

Graphing Linear Equations Using the Intercepts Method

L E S S O N   2 5

You will learn how to:

- use a graph or an equation to find the *x*-intercept and *y*-intercept of a line

- graph a linear equation by using the *x*- and *y*-intercepts

Key Words: *x*-intercept, *y*-intercept

A missile *intercepts* its target. A secret agent *intercepts* a coded message. A defensive back *intercepts* a pass. The word *intercepts* suggests that two things meet. A graphed line may intercept each coordinate axis.

The line shown crosses the *x*-axis at (3, 0). The *x*-coordinate of that point, 3, is called the *x-intercept* of that line. The line crosses the *y*-axis at (0, −2). The *y*-coordinate of that point, −2, is called the *y-intercept* of that line.

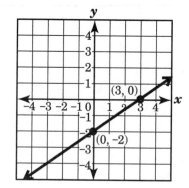

Notice that the ordered pair that contains the *x*-intercept has a *y*-coordinate of 0 because all points on the *x*-axis have a *y*-coordinate of 0. The ordered pair that contains the *y*-intercept has an *x*-coordinate of 0 because all points on the *y*-axis have an *x*-coordinate of 0. You can use the equation of a line and this idea to find the *x*- and *y*-intercepts of the line.

Example: Use the graph to find the *x*- and *y*-intercept of each line.

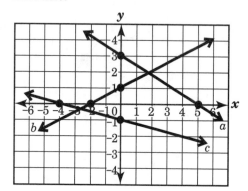

line	x-intercept	y-intercept
a	5	3
b	−2	1
c	−4	−1

line *a* goes through points (5, 0) and (0, 3)

line *b* goes through points (0, 1) and (−2, 0)

line *c* goes through points (−4, 0) and (0, −1)

Example: Find the *x*- and *y*-intercepts of the graph of
$2x + 5y = 20$.

To find the *x*-intercept:

$2x + 5y = 20$

$2x + 5(0) = 20$ ← Substitute 0 for *y*.

$2x = 20$ ← Solve for *x*.

$x = 10$

The *x*-intercept is 10. This corresponds to the point (10, 0).

To find the *y*-intercept:

$2x + 5y = 20$

$2(0) + 5y = 20$ ← Substitute 0 for *x*.

$5y = 20$ ← Solve for *y*.

$y = 4$

The *y*-intercept is 4. This corresponds to the point (0, 4).

Example: The *x*-intercept of a line is -3 and the *y*-intercept is 4. Graph the line.

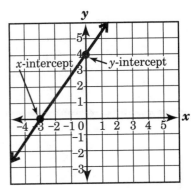

Since the *x*-intercept is -3, the line crosses the *x*-axis at $(-3, 0)$. Since the *y*-intercept is 4, the line crosses the *y*-axis at (0, 4). Plot the points $(-3, 0)$ and (0, 4) and draw a line through the points.

Example: Determine if each equation has an *x*-intercept of 5.

$2x + y = 10$

$2(5) + 0 \stackrel{?}{=} 10$ ← Substitute 5 for *x* and 0 for *y*.

$10 = 10$

Because (5, 0) makes the equation true, $2x + y = 10$ has an *x*-intercept of 5.

$x - 2y = 10$

$5 - 2(0) \stackrel{?}{=} 10$ ← Substitute 5 for *x* and 0 for *y*.

$5 \neq 10$

Because (5, 0) makes the equation false, $x - 2y = 10$ does not have an *x*-intercept of 5.

Self-Test

Circle the letter of the correct answer.

1. Where does the graph of $y = 2x - 6$ cross the *x*-axis?

   A. (6, 0) C. (0, 3)

   B. $(-3, 0)$ D. (3, 0)

2. If the *y*-intercept of a line is 2, which may be an equation for the line?

   A. $y = 2x$ C. $y = x - 2$

   B. $x + y = 2$ D. $2x - y = 4$

Check your answer.

1. *D is correct. To find the x-intercept, substitute 0 for y.*

   $0 = 2x - 6$

   $6 = 2x$

   $3 = x$

   So, the graph crosses the x-axis at (3, 0).

2. *B is correct. If the y-intercept is 2, the line crosses the y-axis at (0, 2).*

   $x + y = 2$

   $0 + 2 = 2$

   $2 = 2$

Lesson 25: Graphing Linear Equations Using the Intercepts Method

Practice

Graphing Linear Equations Using the Intercepts Method

Circle the letter of the correct answer.

1. Where does the graph of $x + y = 4$ cross the x-axis?

   A. $(-4, 0)$
   B. $(0, 4)$
   C. $(0, -4)$
   D. $(4, 0)$

2. Where does the graph of $y = x - 5$ cross the y-axis?

   A. $(0, 5)$
   B. $(0, -5)$
   C. $(5, 0)$
   D. $(-5, 0)$

3. The x-intercept of the graph of $y = 2x + 8$ is which of the following?

   A. -4
   B. 0
   C. 4
   D. 8

4. The y-intercept of the graph of $5x + 7y = 35$ is which of the following?

   A. -7
   B. -5
   C. 5
   D. 7

5. The graph of $2x - 3y = 12$ crosses the x-axis at which of the following?

   A. $(2, 0)$
   B. $(3, 0)$
   C. $(6, 0)$
   D. $(12, 0)$

6. The graph of $4x - 3y = 12$ crosses the y-axis at which point?

   A. $(0, -4)$
   B. $(0, -3)$
   C. $(0, 3)$
   D. $(0, 4)$

7. The x-intercept of the line in the graph is which of the following?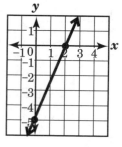

   A. -2
   B. 0
   C. 2
   D. -5

8. The y-intercept of the line in the graph is which of the following?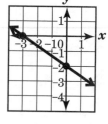

   A. -3
   B. -2
   C. 0
   D. 3

9. The x-intercept of a line is 7. Where does it cross the x-axis?

   A. $(0, 7)$
   B. $(-7, 0)$
   C. $(0, -7)$
   D. $(7, 0)$

10. The y-intercept of a line is -5. Where does it cross the y-axis?

    A. $(-5, 0)$
    B. $(0, -5)$
    C. $(5, 0)$
    D. $(0, 5)$

100

Lesson 25: Graphing Linear Equations Using the Intercepts Method

11. If the y-intercept of a line is 1, which may be an equation for the line?

A. $x - y = 1$
B. $x + y = 1$
C. $y = 2x - 1$
D. $3x + y = 3$

12. If the y-intercept of a line is -6, which may be an equation for the line?

A. $x - y = 6$
B. $6x + y = 6$
C. $y - 6 = x$
D. $2x + 6y = 12$

13. If the x-intercept of a line is 4, which may be an equation for the line?

A. $y = 2x + 8$
B. $x - 2y = 8$
C. $2x - y = 8$
D. $y = x + 4$

14. If the x-intercept of a line is -3, which may be an equation for the line?

A. $3x + y = 9$
B. $3x - y = 9$
C. $y = 9 - 3x$
D. $y = 3x + 9$

15. Which equation has an x-intercept of 3 and a y-intercept of -3?

A. $x = y$
B. $x + y = 3$
C. $x + y = 0$
D. $x - y = 3$

16. Which equation has an x-intercept of 3 and a y-intercept of -2?

A. $3x + 2y = 5$
B. $3x - 2y = 6$
C. $2x - 3y = 6$
D. $2x + 3y = 6$

17. Which equation has an x-intercept of -2 and a y-intercept of -5?

A. $x + y = -7$
B. $5x + 2y = -10$
C. $5x - 2y = -10$
D. $2x - 5y = -10$

18. Which statement is true about the graph?

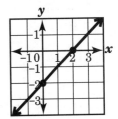

A. It has an y-intercept of 2.
B. It has an x-intercept of -2.
C. It has an x-intercept of 2.
D. It has an x-intercept of 0.

19. Which statement is true about the graph?

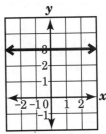

A. It has a y-intercept of -3.
B. It has a y-intercept of 3.
C. It has a y-intercept of 0.
D. It does not have a y-intercept.

Graphing Linear Functions and Applying Slope

LESSON 26

> You will learn how to:
> - find the slope of a line
> - write a linear equation using slope and *y*-intercept
> - graph a linear function using slope and *y*-intercept

Key Words: slope, rise, run, slope-intercept form

A set of stairs, a roof, and a ramp all have steepness. The measure of the steepness of a line is called its slope. The **slope** of a line is the ratio of the rise to the run. The **rise** is the vertical change from one point to another on the line which can be found by subtracting *y*-coordinates. The **run** is the horizontal change which can be found by subtracting *x*-coordinates.

$$slope = \frac{rise}{run}$$

$$\text{Slope} = \frac{\text{rise}}{\text{run}} = \frac{\text{vertical change}}{\text{horizontal change}} = \frac{\text{difference between } y\text{-coordinates}}{\text{difference between } x\text{-coordinates}}.$$

Example: A drawing of a set of stairs is placed on a coordinate plane, and a line is drawn as shown. What is the slope of the line?

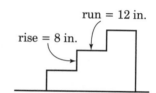

The slope can be calculated by using the coordinates of any two points on a line.

Using *A* and *C*, slope $= \dfrac{\text{difference between } y\text{-coordinates}}{\text{difference between } x\text{-coordinates}} = \dfrac{16 - 0}{24 - 0} = \dfrac{16}{24} = \dfrac{2}{3}.$

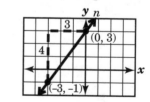

Using *C* and *D*, slope $= \dfrac{\text{difference between } y\text{-coordinates}}{\text{difference between } x\text{-coordinates}} = \dfrac{24 - 16}{36 - 24} = \dfrac{8}{12} = \dfrac{2}{3}.$

Notice that the slope of the line is the same, even though two different sets of points were used.

Example: What is the slope of line *m*?

Slope $= \dfrac{3 - 1}{7 - 3} = \dfrac{2}{4} = \dfrac{1}{2}$

Notice that the lines slant up from left to right. Any line that slants up from left to right has a positive slope.

Example: What is the slope of line *n*?

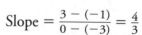

Slope $= \dfrac{3 - (-1)}{0 - (-3)} = \dfrac{4}{3}$

Example: Find the slope of the line $y = -2x + 4$.

(2, 0) and (0, 4) can be used. Slope $= \frac{4 - 0}{0 - 2} = \frac{4}{-2} = -2$

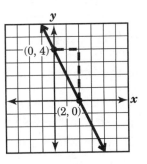

Notice that the line slants down from left to right. Any line that slants down from left to right has a negative slope.

In the equation $y = -2x + 4$, the coefficient of x, -2, is the slope of the line. The y-intercept, where the line crosses the y-axis, is 4.

For any equation written in the form $y = mx + b$, m is the slope of the graph, and b is the y-intercept.

$y = mx + b$ is called *slope-intercept form*.

$$y = -2x + 4$$
$$\uparrow \qquad \uparrow$$
$$\text{slope} \quad y\text{-intercept}$$
$$\downarrow \qquad \downarrow$$
$$y = mx + b$$

Example: Use slope-intercept form to write an equation of the line shown.

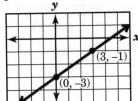

Slope $= \frac{-1 - (-3)}{3 - 0} = \frac{2}{3}$.
The y-intercept is -3. The equation of the line is $y = \frac{2}{3}x + (-3)$, or $y = \frac{2}{3}x - 3$.

Example: Use slope-intercept form to graph the line with the given equation.

$$y = -\frac{3}{2}x + 2$$

The y-intercept is 2, so plot the point (0, 2). The slope of the line is $-\frac{3}{2}$ or $\frac{-3}{2}$. Count 3 units down from (0, 2), and then 2 units right to plot another point. Graph the line through the two points.

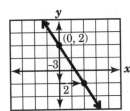

Self-Test

Circle the letter of the correct answer.

Which equation describes the graph shown below?

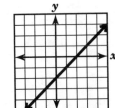

A. $y = x - 2$

B. $y = x + 2$

C. $y = 2x + 1$

D. $y = 2x - 1$

Check your answer.

A is correct.
From the graph, the slope of the line is 1, and the y-intercept is -2. So, the equation is
$y = 1x + (-2)$, or $y = x - 2$.

Practice

Graphing Linear Functions and Applying Slope

Circle the letter of the correct answer.

1. The flight path of an airplane right after takeoff has a run of 100 yards and a rise of 20 yards. Which could be the slope of the flight path?

    A. $\frac{1}{80}$

    B. $\frac{1}{20}$

    C. $\frac{1}{5}$

    D. 5

2. A roof rises 6 feet for every 12 feet of horizontal change. Which could be the slope of the roof?

    A. $\frac{1}{12}$

    B. $\frac{1}{6}$

    C. $\frac{1}{2}$

    D. 2

3. What is the slope of the line?

    A. $\frac{3}{2}$

    B. $\frac{2}{3}$

    C. $-\frac{2}{3}$

    D. $-\frac{3}{2}$

    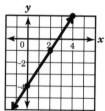

4. What is the slope of the line?

    A. $-\frac{5}{4}$

    B. $-\frac{4}{5}$

    C. $\frac{4}{5}$

    D. $\frac{5}{4}$

    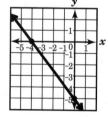

5. What is the slope of the line?

    A. -3

    B. 3

    C. $\frac{1}{3}$

    D. $-\frac{1}{3}$

    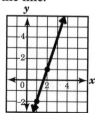

6. What is the slope of the line containing points $A(0, -4)$ and $B(2, 0)$?

    A. -4

    B. -2

    C. $\frac{1}{2}$

    D. 2

7. Which graph has a slope of 3?

    A. line a

    B. line b

    C. line c

    D. line d

8. Which graph has a slope of $-\frac{4}{3}$?

    A. line a

    B. line b

    C. line c

    D. line d

9. What is the slope of the line whose equation is $y = \frac{3}{5}x - 1$?

    A. -1

    B. $\frac{3}{5}$

    C. $\frac{5}{3}$

    D. 3

10. What is the slope of the line whose equation is $y = 2x - 5$?

    A. -5

    B. -3

    C. -2

    D. 2

11. Which equation describes the graph shown?

A. $y = 2x$

B. $y = 2x + 2$

C. $y = x + 2$

D. $y = x - 2$

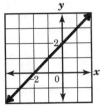

12. Which equation describes the graph shown?

A. $y = -\frac{3}{2}x + 5$

B. $y = -\frac{2}{3}x + 5$

C. $y = \frac{2}{3}x + 5$

D. $y = \frac{3}{2}x + 5$

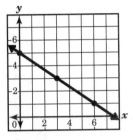

13. Which equation describes the graph shown?

A. $y = 3x - 3$

B. $y = 3x + 3$

C. $y = -3x + 3$

D. $y = -3x - 3$

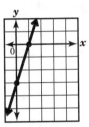

14. The slope of the line joining $(0, 4)$ and $(2, 3)$ is

A. -2

B. $-\frac{1}{2}$

C. $\frac{1}{2}$

D. 2

15. The slope of the line joining $(-3, 2)$ and $(1, 5)$ is

A. $-\frac{4}{3}$

B. $-\frac{3}{4}$

C. $\frac{3}{4}$

D. $\frac{4}{3}$

16. The slope of the line joining $(-2, 0)$ and $(0, 6)$ is

A. -3

B. $-\frac{1}{3}$

C. $\frac{1}{3}$

D. 3

17. Which equation describes the line whose slope is 4 and y-intercept is -1?

A. $y = -4x + 1$

B. $y = 4x + 1$

C. $y = -4x - 1$

D. $y = 4x - 1$

18. Which equation describes the line whose slope is -2 and y-intercept is 2?

A. $y = -2x + 2$

B. $y = 2x + 2$

C. $y = 2x - 2$

D. $y = -2x - 2$

19. What is an equation of the line that includes the point $(3, -8)$ and has a slope of $-\frac{2}{3}$?

A. $y = -\frac{2}{3}x + 6$

B. $y = \frac{2}{3}x + 6$

C. $y = \frac{2}{3}x - 6$

D. $y = -\frac{2}{3}x - 6$

20. What is an equation of the line that includes the point $(10, 5)$ and has a slope of $\frac{1}{5}$?

A. $y = -\frac{1}{5}x + 3$

B. $y = \frac{1}{5}x + 3$

C. $y = \frac{1}{5}x - 3$

D. $y = -\frac{1}{5}x - 3$

Identifying Parallel Lines

LESSON 27

You will learn how to:
- use slope to determine if lines are parallel
- determine the slope of a line that is parallel to a given line
- use slope to write the equation of a line parallel to a given line

Key Words: parallel lines

Two lines in a plane that do not intersect are called *parallel lines.*

Example: Which lines on the graph are parallel? What is true about the slopes of parallel lines?

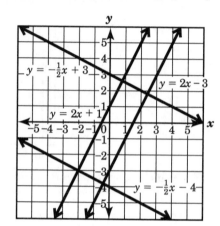

The lines $y = 2x - 3$ and $y = 2x + 1$ are parallel.
They each have a slope of 2.

The lines $y = -\frac{1}{2}x + 3$ and $y = -\frac{1}{2}x - 4$ are parallel.
They each have a slope of $-\frac{1}{2}$.

Parallel lines have the same slope, and lines with the same slope are parallel.

Example: Which of the following lines are parallel?

$y = -2x + 1,\ y = 2x + 1,\ y = -2x - 7,\ y = \frac{1}{2}x - 7$

The lines $y = -2x + 1$ and $y = -2x - 7$ are parallel because they have the same slope. They each have a slope of –2.

Example: What is the slope of any line parallel to the line $y = \frac{3}{4}x + 5$?

The slope of the line $y = \frac{3}{4}x + 5$ is $\frac{3}{4}$.
Therefore, the slope of any line parallel to the line $y = \frac{3}{4}x + 5$ is $\frac{3}{4}$.

Example: What is the slope of any line parallel to the line $3x + y = 6$?

To determine the slope, get the equation in the form $y = mx + b$.
$3x + y = 6$ ← Write the original equation of the line.
$y = -3x + 6$ ← Solve for y by subtracting $3x$ from both sides.

The slope of the line $3x + y = 6$ is -3.
If two lines are parallel, they have the same slope.
So, the slope of any line parallel to the line $3x + y = 6$ is -3.

Lesson 27: Identifying Parallel Lines

Example: Write an equation of the line which has a
y-intercept of 8 and is parallel to the line
$y = -2x - 4$.

For an equation in the form $y = mx + b$, the slope of its graph is
m and the y-intercept is b.

The slope of $y = -2x - 4$ is -2, so any line parallel to it has a
slope of -2.

The parallel line must have a slope of -2 and a y-intercept of 8.

So, the equation of the line is $y = -2x + 8$.

Example: Write an equation of the line which is parallel to
the line $y = -\frac{3}{2}x + 1$ and passes through the
point $(0, -3)$.

It has the same slope as the line $y = -\frac{3}{2}x + 1$, so it has slope $-\frac{3}{2}$.

The line passes through $(0, -3)$, so it has y-intercept -3.

Therefore, an equation of the line is $y = -\frac{3}{2}x - 3$.

Self-Test
Circle the letter of the correct answer.

1. What is the slope of a line parallel to
$y = -2x + 1$?

A. -2 C. 1

B. $-\frac{1}{2}$ D. 2

2. What is an equation of a line which has
y-intercept -2 and is parallel to the line
$y = 3x - 1$?

A. $y = -2x - 1$ C. $y = 3x + 2$

B. $y = -2x - 3$ D. $y = 3x - 2$

Check your answer.

1. *A is correct.*

   *For an equation in the form y = mx + b,
   m is the slope of its graph. The slope of
   the line y = −2x + 1 is −2. If two lines are
   parallel, they have the same slope.*

   *Therefore, the slope of a line parallel to the
   line y = −2x + 1 is also −2.*

2. *D is correct.*

   *If two lines are parallel, they have the
   same slope. The slope of the line
   y = 3x − 1 is 3. The parallel line must have
   a slope of 3 and a y-intercept of −2. So,
   the equation of the line is y = 3x − 2.*

Practice

Identifying Parallel Lines

Circle the letter of the correct answer.

1. Which of the following statements describes parallel lines?

    A. They have the same y-intercept, but different slopes.

    B. They have the same slope, but different y-intercepts.

    C. They have opposite slopes, but the same x-intercept.

    D. They have opposite x-intercepts, but the same y-intercept.

2. What is the slope of a line parallel to the line $y = \frac{1}{2}x - 3$?

    A. -3

    B. $-\frac{1}{2}$

    C. $\frac{1}{2}$

    D. 2

3. What is the slope of a line parallel to the line $y = -\frac{5}{4}x + 2$?

    A. $-\frac{5}{4}$

    B. $-\frac{4}{5}$

    C. $\frac{4}{5}$

    D. $\frac{5}{4}$

4. What is the slope of a line parallel to the line $y = x + 7$?

    A. -7

    B. -1

    C. 1

    D. 7

5. What is the slope of a line parallel to the line $5x + y = 5$?

    A. -5

    B. -1

    C. 1

    D. 5

6. What is the slope of a line parallel to the line $y - 2x = -1$?

    A. -2

    B. -1

    C. 1

    D. 2

7. Which is an equation of the line that has a y-intercept of 4 and is parallel to the line $y = \frac{4}{3}x - 3$?

    A. $y = -\frac{4}{3}x - 4$

    B. $y = \frac{4}{3}x - 4$

    C. $y = \frac{4}{3}x + 4$

    D. $y = -\frac{4}{3}x - 3$

8. Which is an equation of the line that has a y-intercept of -1 and is parallel to the line $y = -4x + 4$?

    A. $y = -4x + 1$

    B. $y = -4x - 1$

    C. $y = 4x - 1$

    D. $y = 4x + 4$

Lesson 27: Identifying Parallel Lines

9. Which is an equation of the line that has a y-intercept of -3 and is parallel to the line $y = 2x + 1$?

A. $y = -3x + 1$

B. $y = -2x - 3$

C. $y = -3x - 1$

D. $y = 2x - 3$

10. Which is an equation of the line that has a y-intercept of 6 and is parallel to the line $x + y = 3$?

A. $y = -x - 3$

B. $y = -x + 6$

C. $y = x - 3$

D. $y = x + 3$

11. Which is an equation of the line that has a y-intercept of -1 and is parallel to the line $3x + y = 3$?

A. $y = -3x - 1$

B. $y = -3x + 1$

C. $y = 3x - 1$

D. $y = 3x + 1$

12. Which is an equation of the line that is parallel to the line $y = -x - 6$ and passes through the point $(0, 8)$?

A. $y = x - 8$

B. $y = x + 8$

C. $y = -x - 8$

D. $y = -x + 8$

13. Which is an equation of the line which is parallel to the line $y = \frac{1}{3}x + 1$ and passes through the point $(0, -2)$?

A. $y = \frac{1}{3}x - 2$

B. $y = 2x + \frac{1}{3}$

C. $y = \frac{1}{3}x + 2$

D. $y = 3x - 2$

14. Which of the following lines is not parallel to the other three lines?

A. $y = -\frac{5}{2}x - 5$

B. $y = -\frac{5}{2}x + 1$

C. $y = \frac{5}{2}x - 4$

D. $y = -\frac{5}{2}x + 2$

15. Which is an equation of the line that is parallel to the line $4x + y = 7$ and passes through the point $(0, -3)$?

A. $y = 4x - 7$

B. $y = -4x + 3$

C. $y = -4x - 3$

D. $y = -4x - 7$

16. Which of the following lines is not parallel to the other three lines?

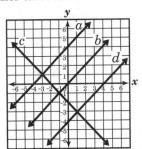

A. line a

B. line b

C. line c

D. line d

Graphing and Interpreting Quantitative Relationships

LESSON 28

You will learn how to:

• interpret the graph of a quantitative relationship

• represent a quantitative relationship by using a graph

Key Words: line graph, trend

Ronnie's bank sent her a graph to show the average daily balance in her checking account for a period of 7 months.

The graph is a line graph. In a *line graph*, data are represented by points. The points are connected by line segments.

Line graphs are often used to show *trends* or patterns of change over time, where the horizontal axis represents time. The steepness of the line segments shows how much the data change. A very steep line segment shows a big change. A less steep line segment shows a lesser change. A horizontal line segment shows there is no change.

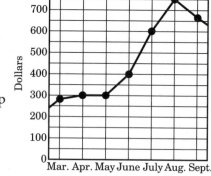

Average Daily Balance

Example: Between which two average daily balances was there no change?

The line segment between the April amount and the May amount is horizontal. There was no change in the average daily balance.

Example: Between which two monthly figures was there the greatest increase in the average daily balance?

The line segment between June and July rises to the right, and is the steepest. The greatest increase occurred between June and July.

Some situations can be graphed as linear equations. Information such as the slope or *y*-intercept can be used to solve problems.

Example: A store is having a discount sale and is selling shirts by the pound. A package weighing three pounds costs $6, a package weighing four pounds costs $8, and a package weighing seven pounds costs $14. Determine the cost of one pound of shirts.

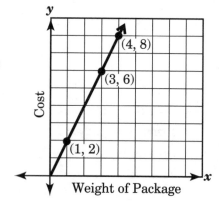

One method is to find the slope: $\frac{rise}{run} = \frac{2}{1} = 2$. So, for every increase of one pound, the cost increases $2.
One pound of shirts costs $2.

Example: Matthew does not feel well. His temperature was 101°F at 8 A.M. His temperature remained steady at 102°F from 9 A.M. through noon. At 2 P.M., his temperature was 99°F. Which graph represents this situation?

Graph A
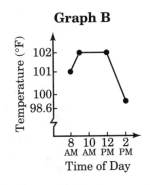

Graph B
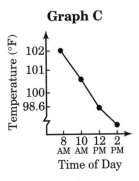

Graph C

The correct graph, Graph B, shows an increase between 8 A.M. and 9 A.M., then a constant section, then a drop.

Self-Test

Circle the letter of the correct answer.

1. Which day marks the end of a decreasing trend and the beginning of an increasing trend in flower sales?

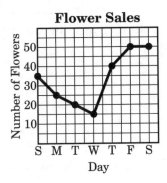

A. Tuesday
B. Wednesday
C. Thursday
D. Friday

2. A car travels at 40 miles per hour and then stops at a traffic light. Which graph represents this situation?

A.
C.

B.
D.

Check your answer.

1. *B is correct.*

   Wednesday is the low point on the graph, indicating the end of a decreasing trend and the beginning of an increasing trend.

2. *A is correct.*

   The car travels at a constant speed, and then the speed declines until the car stops.

Practice

Graphing and Interpreting Quantitative Relationships

Circle the letter of the correct answer.

1. Karen went bike riding. The graph below shows the relationship between her speed and her time.

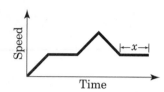

What does the part of the graph marked "*x*" represent?

A. a time when she was accelerating

B. a time when she was decelerating

C. a time when she was biking at a constant rate

D. a time when she was resting

2. The graph shows the population of a town during the second half of the twentieth century.

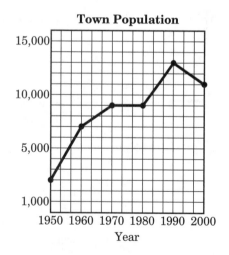

Which of the following is true about the decade from 1980 to 1990?

A. The population remained the same.

B. The population increased.

C. The population decreased.

D. Everybody moved away.

3. Which month marks the end of an increasing trend and the beginning of a decreasing trend in automobile sales?

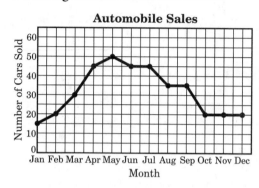

A. April

B. May

C. July

D. September

4. Beth jogs uphill at a constant speed. Then her speed increases as she runs downhill. Which graph represents this situation?

A.   C.

B.   D.

5. Jack turned on the air conditioner. The room got cooler, and then the temperature remained constant. Which graph represents this situation?

A.   C.

B.   D.

6. A bus makes several stops to let off and pick up passengers. Which graph represents this situation?

A.

C.

B.

D.

7. The cost of a taxi ride by each of two different cab companies is shown.

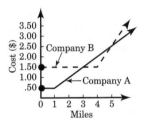

Company B costs less than Company A for

A. all rides

B. a ride between 3 miles and 5 miles

C. all rides of more than 3 miles

D. rides of less than 3 miles

8. The graph shows the sales of two toy companies.

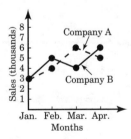

In which month did the sales of Company A exceed the sales of Company B?

A. January

B. February

C. March

D. April

9. The graph shows the distances traveled by two cars that left the same place at the same time, and traveled the same route.

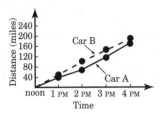

At what time is the difference in distance between the two cars the greatest?

A. 1 P.M.

B. 2 P.M.

C. 3 P.M.

D. 4 P.M.

10. A car maintains a steady speed for a five-mile trip. After three minutes, it had traveled one mile and after nine minutes, it had traveled three miles. How far did it travel each minute?

A. $\frac{1}{5}$ mile

B. $\frac{1}{3}$ mile

C. 3 miles

D. 5 miles

11. The graph below shows the change in price of beef as the weight increases. What is the price of one pound of beef?

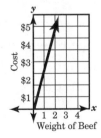

A. $1.50

B. $1.75

C. $2.25

D. $2.50

Solving Systems of Linear Equations I

LESSON 29

You will learn how to:

- determine if an ordered pair is a solution to a system of linear equations
- solve a system of linear equations by graphing
- identify a system of linear equations as having exactly one solution, no solution, or an infinite number of solutions

Key Words: solution to a system of linear equations in two variables

Recall that a system of equations represents a set of conditions. A *solution to a system of linear equations in two variables* is an ordered pair that makes both equations true.

Example: Is (3, 1) a solution to the system of equations?

$$2x + 4y = 10$$
$$2(3) + 4(1) \stackrel{?}{=} 10$$
$$6 + 4 \stackrel{?}{=} 10$$
$$10 = 10$$

$$-3x + 7y = -2$$
$$-3(3) + 7(1) \stackrel{?}{=} -2$$
$$-9 + 7 \stackrel{?}{=} -2$$
$$-2 = -2$$

$$\begin{cases} 2x + 4y = 10 \\ -3x + 7y = -2 \end{cases}$$

(3, 1) makes both equations true. It is a solution.

One method of solving a system of two linear equations is to graph the equations on the same coordinate plane. If the graphs intersect, then the point of intersection represents the solution to the system. In that case, there is exactly one solution to the system.

Example: Solve the system of equations by graphing.

$$\begin{cases} x + y = 7 \\ -x + 3y = -9 \end{cases}$$

Use the intercept method to graph each equation.

The graph of $x + y = 7$ has intercepts at (0, 7) and (7, 0).

The graph of $-x + 3y = 9$ has intercepts at (0, 3) and (-9, 0).

The solution to the system of equations is (3, 4) because the lines intersect at that point. You can check this solution by substituting 3 for x and 4 for y into both equations and verifying that they make both equations true.

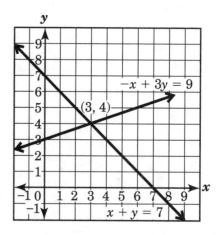

$$x + y = 7$$
$$3 + 4 \stackrel{?}{=} 7$$
$$7 = 7$$

$$-x + 3y = 9$$
$$-3 + 3(4) \stackrel{?}{=} 9$$
$$-3 + 12 \stackrel{?}{=} 9$$
$$9 = 9$$

(3, 4) is the solution because it makes both equations true.

A system of equations whose graphs are parallel lines has no solution because the lines do not intersect.

A system whose graphs are the same line has an infinite number of solutions because every point on the line is a solution.

Examples:

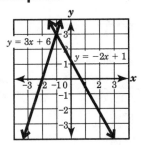

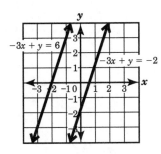

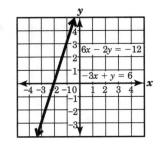

Exactly One Solution   No Solution   Infinite Number of Solutions

One way to determine the number of solutions is to write both equations in slope-intercept form.

Examples: Determine the number of solutions for each system.

$$\begin{cases} 2x + y = 7 \\ x + y = 10 \end{cases} \qquad \begin{cases} y = -2x + 7 \\ y = -x + 10 \end{cases}$$ The lines have different slopes, so they intersect. There is exactly one solution.

$$\begin{cases} -3x - y = 5 \\ y = -3x + 6 \end{cases} \qquad \begin{cases} y = -3x - 5 \\ y = -3x + 6 \end{cases}$$ The lines have the same slope, but different y-intercepts, so they are parallel. There is no solution.

$$\begin{cases} 2x + y = 5 \\ 3y = -6x + 15 \end{cases} \qquad \begin{cases} y = -2x + 5 \\ y = -2x + 5 \end{cases}$$ The equations have the same graph. There are an infinite number of solutions.

Self-Test

Circle the letter of the correct answer.

Which statement is true about the system?

$$\begin{cases} x + y = 5 \\ x + y = -3 \end{cases}$$

A. There is no solution.

B. There are an infinite number of solutions.

C. $(0, 5)$ is the only solution.

D. $(0, -3)$ is the only solution.

Check your answer.

A is correct.

$$\begin{cases} x + y = 5 \\ x + y = -3 \end{cases} \rightarrow \begin{cases} y = -x + 5 \\ y = -x - 3 \end{cases}$$

The lines are parallel because they have the same slope, -1, but different y-intercepts.

There is no solution.

Practice

Solving Systems of Linear Equations I

Circle the letter of the correct answer.

1. Use the graphs to find the solution to the system of equations.

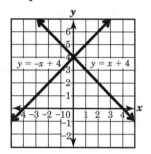

A. $(0, 4)$

B. $(-4, 0)$

C. $(0, -4)$

D. $(4, 0)$

2. Use the graphs to find the solution to the system of equations.

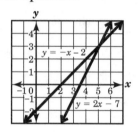

A. $(-2, -7)$

B. $(5, 3)$

C. $(2, 3.5)$

D. $(-1, 1)$

3. The point $(-1, 0)$ is the solution to which of these systems of equations?

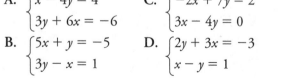

A. $\begin{cases} x - 4y = 4 \\ 3y + 6x = -6 \end{cases}$ C. $\begin{cases} -2x + 7y = 2 \\ 3x - 4y = 0 \end{cases}$

B. $\begin{cases} 5x + y = -5 \\ 3y - x = 1 \end{cases}$ D. $\begin{cases} 2y + 3x = -3 \\ x - y = 1 \end{cases}$

4. Which statement is true about the following system of equations?

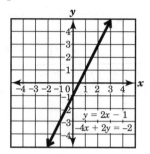

A. There is no solution.

B. $(0, -1)$ is the only solution.

C. There are an infinite number of solutions.

D. $(-1, 0)$ is the only solution.

5. Use the graphs to find the solution to the system of equations.

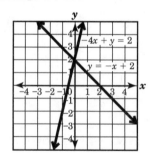

A. $(0, 2)$

B. $(-2, 0)$

C. $(0, -2)$

D. $(2, 0)$

6. The point $(2, 3)$ is the solution to which of these systems of equations?

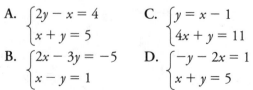

A. $\begin{cases} 2y - x = 4 \\ x + y = 5 \end{cases}$ C. $\begin{cases} y = x - 1 \\ 4x + y = 11 \end{cases}$

B. $\begin{cases} 2x - 3y = -5 \\ x - y = 1 \end{cases}$ D. $\begin{cases} -y - 2x = 1 \\ x + y = 5 \end{cases}$

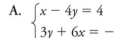

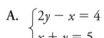

116

Lesson 29: Solving Systems of Linear Equations I

7. Which statement is true about the following system of equations?

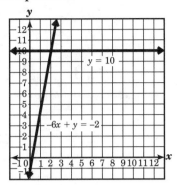

A. There is no solution.

B. (0, –2) is the only solution.

C. There are an infinite number of solutions.

D. (2, 10) is the only solution.

8. Which statement is true about the following system of equations?

$$\begin{cases} x + y = 7 \\ 2x + y = 9 \end{cases}$$

A. There is no solution.

B. (2, 5) is the only solution.

C. There are an infinite number of solutions.

D. (5, 2) is the only solution.

9. Which statement is true about the following system of equations?

$$\begin{cases} x + y = 5 \\ x + y = -5 \end{cases}$$

A. There is no solution.

B. (2, 3) is the only solution.

C. There are an infinite number of solutions.

D. (–3, –2) is the only solution.

10. Which statement is true about the following system of equations?

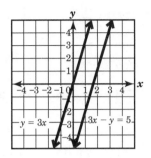

A. There is no solution.

B. (0, 0) is the only solution.

C. There are an infinite number of solutions.

D. (0, −4) is the only solution.

11. Which statement is true about the following system of equations?

$$\begin{cases} 3x - 2y = 4 \\ -9x + 6y = -12 \end{cases}$$

A. There is no solution.

B. (4, 4) is the only solution.

C. There are an infinite number of solutions.

D. (−4, −4) is the only solution.

12. Which of these systems of equations has (−9, −3) as its solution?

A. $\begin{cases} x + y = 12 \\ 2x - y = -15 \end{cases}$ C. $\begin{cases} -5x + 7y = 24 \\ x - 3y = -9 \end{cases}$

B. $\begin{cases} 4x - 3y = -27 \\ y - x = 6 \end{cases}$ D. $\begin{cases} x + y = -12 \\ 2x - 3y = -27 \end{cases}$

13. The point (1, 4) is the solution to which of these systems of equations?

A. $\begin{cases} y + 7x = 29 \\ 3x + y = 0 \end{cases}$ C. $\begin{cases} 2y = x + 7 \\ -4x + y = 9 \end{cases}$

B. $\begin{cases} 2y + x = 3 \\ y = 5 - x \end{cases}$ D. $\begin{cases} -x - y = -5 \\ 2x + y = 6 \end{cases}$

Solving Systems of Linear Equations II

LESSON 30

You will learn how to:

• solve systems of linear equations by using the substitution method

• solve systems of linear equations by using the elimination method

Key Words: substitution method, elimination method

In a previous lesson, you learned how to solve a system of equations using the graphing method.

$$\begin{cases} 2x + y = 5 \\ x - y = 1 \end{cases}$$

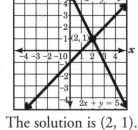

Another method of solving a system of equations is the *substitution method.*

Example: Solve using the substitution method.

$$\begin{cases} 2x + y = 5 \\ x - y = 1 \end{cases}$$ The solution is (2, 1).

Solve an equation for one of the variables. If there is a variable with a coefficient of 1, solve for that variable.	Substitute the expression found in step 1 into the other equation and solve for the variable.	Substitute the value from step 2 into either of the original equations and solve for the other variable.
$2x + y = 5$ $y = -2x + 5$	$x - y = 1$ $x - (-2x + 5) = 1$ $x + 2x - 5 = 1$ $x = 2$	$2x + y = 5$ $2(2) + y = 5$ $4 + y = 5$ $y = 1$

The solution is (2, 1).

The *elimination method* is a third way to solve a system of equations. If a variable has the same coefficient in both equations, subtract. If a variable has opposite coefficients, add.

Example: Solve using the elimination method.

$$\begin{cases} 2x + y = 5 \\ x - y = 1 \end{cases}$$

The coefficients of y are opposites (1 and -1), so add the equations to eliminate y.

Add to eliminate y.	Solve for x.	Solve for y.
$2x + y = 5$ $\underline{+\ x - y = 1}$ $3x\quad\ \ = 6$	$3x = 6$ $x = 2$	$2x + y = 5$ $2(2) + y = 5$ $4 + y = 5$ $y = 1$

The solution is (2, 1).

Example: Solve using the elimination method.

$$\begin{cases} 5x + y = 15 \\ -2x + 4y = -6 \end{cases}$$

Neither variable has equal or opposite coefficients. However, if you multiply both sides of the top equation by -4, the y-coefficients will be opposites.

Multiply.	Add and solve for x.	Solve for y.
$\begin{cases} -4(5x + y) = -4(15) \\ -2x + 4y = -6 \end{cases} \rightarrow \begin{cases} -20x - 4y = -60 \\ -2x + 4y = -6 \end{cases}$	$\begin{aligned} -20x - 4y &= -60 \\ + -2x + 4y &= -6 \\ \hline -22x &= -66 \\ x &= 3 \end{aligned}$	$\begin{aligned} 5x + y &= 15 \\ 5(3) + y &= 15 \\ y &= 0 \end{aligned}$

The solution is $(3, 0)$.

You may also determine how many solutions a system of equations has by using either method. A false statement implies that there is no solution and a true statement implies an infinite number of solutions.

Examples: How many solutions does the system of equations have?

$$\begin{cases} -3x + y = 6 \\ -3x + y = -2 \end{cases}$$

$$\begin{cases} -3x + y = 6 \\ 6x - 2y = -12 \end{cases}$$

Use the elimination method.

Subtract.
$$\begin{aligned} -3x + y &= 6 \\ - (-3x + y &= -2) \\ \hline 0 &= 8 \end{aligned}$$

$0 = 8$ is a false statement. This system has no solution.

Use the substitution method.

Solve for y.   Substitute and solve for x.
$$\begin{aligned} -3x + y &= 6 & 6x - 2y &= -12 \\ y &= 6 + 3x & 6x - 2(6 + 3x) &= -12 \\ & & -12 &= -12 \end{aligned}$$

$-12 = -12$ is a true statement. This system has an infinite number of solutions.

Self-Test

Circle the letter of the correct answer.

What is the solution to the system of equations?

$$\begin{cases} 3x - 2y = 1 \\ x + 4y = 5 \end{cases}$$

A. $(-3, 2)$ C. $(9, -1)$

B. $(0, -\frac{1}{2})$ D. $(1, 1)$

Check your answer.

D is correct.

$$\begin{aligned} x + 4y &= 5 & 3x - 2y &= 1 & x + 4y &= 5 \\ x &= 5 - 4y & 3(5 - 4y) - 2y &= 1 & x + 4(1) &= 5 \\ & & y &= 1 & x &= 1 \end{aligned}$$

Practice

Solving Systems of Linear Equations II

Circle the letter of the correct answer.

1. Find the solution to the system of equations.

$$\begin{cases} x - y = 1 \\ x + 2y = 25 \end{cases}$$

  A. $(4, 4)$

  B. $(1, 12)$

  C. $(9, 8)$

  D. $(8, 7)$

2. What is the solution to the system of equations?

$$\begin{cases} x + y = -9 \\ 2x + 3y = -20 \end{cases}$$

  A. $(-10, 1)$

  B. $(-5, 2)$

  C. $(-7, -2)$

  D. $(3, -1)$

3. What is the solution to the system of equations?

$$\begin{cases} x = -3y \\ x + y = 2 \end{cases}$$

  A. $(3, -1)$

  B. $(-5, 7)$

  C. $(0, 0)$

  D. $(21, -7)$

4. Find the solution to the system of equations.

$$\begin{cases} 2x + 3y = 4 \\ -3x + 3y = -6 \end{cases}$$

  A. $(-1, 1)$

  B. $(-1, -1)$

  C. $(2, 0)$

  D. no solution

5. What is the solution to the system of equations?

$$\begin{cases} x + 3y = 9 \\ 4x - 2y = -6 \end{cases}$$

  A. $(0, 3)$

  B. $(6, 1)$

  C. $(-3, 4)$

  D. $(2, 1)$

6. What is the solution to the system of equations?

$$\begin{cases} 4x + 3y = -29 \\ -4x + 5y = 37 \end{cases}$$

  A. $(-8, 1)$

  B. $(8, 7)$

  C. $(6, 5)$

  D. an infinite number of solutions

7. What is the solution to the system of equations?

$$\begin{cases} y = x + 7 \\ 2x + y = -14 \end{cases}$$

  A. $(5, -2)$

  B. $(-7, 0)$

  C. $(-6, -2)$

  D. $(8, 1)$

8. Find the solution to the system of equations.

$$\begin{cases} x = -y - 12 \\ 2x - y = -15 \end{cases}$$

  A. $(-10, 2)$

  B. $(-13, 1)$

  C. $(-9, -3)$

  D. no solution

9. Find the solution to the system of equations.

$$\begin{cases} 2x - y = 2 \\ 3x - 2y = 0 \end{cases}$$

- A. $(4, -2)$
- B. $(4, 6)$
- C. $(2, 3)$
- D. $(-5, -12)$

10. Find the solution to the system of equations.

$$\begin{cases} y = 4x - 16 \\ 2x + 3y = 8 \end{cases}$$

- A. $(-2, 4)$
- B. $(1, -8)$
- C. $(0, 0)$
- D. $(4, 0)$

11. What is the solution to the system of equations?

$$\begin{cases} x - y = 7 \\ -x + 3y = -13 \end{cases}$$

- A. $(4, -3)$
- B. $(2, -7)$
- C. $(5, -1)$
- D. no solution

12. Find the solution to the system of equations.

$$\begin{cases} -2x - 2y = 6 \\ x + y = -3 \end{cases}$$

- A. $(10, 7)$
- B. $(-3, 0)$
- C. $(1, -8)$
- D. an infinite number of solutions

13. What is the solution to the system of equations?

$$\begin{cases} x + 3y = 5 \\ -2x - 9y = -7 \end{cases}$$

- A. $(1, -8)$
- B. $(2, 1)$
- C. $(8, -1)$
- D. $(-1, 6)$

14. Find the solution to the system of equations.

$$\begin{cases} x + 3y = 5 \\ 2x - 4y = -10 \end{cases}$$

- A. $(3, 4)$
- B. $(-5, 0)$
- C. $(2, 1)$
- D. $(-1, 2)$

15. What is the solution to the system of equations?

$$\begin{cases} 4x + 6y = -10 \\ -x + 4y = 8 \end{cases}$$

- A. $(4, 3)$
- B. $(-4, 1)$
- C. $(-1, -1)$
- D. $(-2, 0)$

16. Find the solution to the system of equations.

$$\begin{cases} -2x - y = 11 \\ 3x - 3y = -39 \end{cases}$$

- A. $(10, -3)$
- B. $(1, 1)$
- C. $(-8, 5)$
- D. $(-5, -1)$

Solving Systems of Linear Inequalities

LESSON 31

You will learn how to:

- graph the solution set of a linear inequality
- graph the solution set of a system of linear inequalities

You know that the graph of a linear equation is a line. The graph of the solution set of a linear inequality is the part of the coordinate plane that contains all the solutions to the inequality.

Consider the linear inequality $y + 2x \leq 50$. If you replace the inequality symbol with an equal symbol, you get the equation $y + 2x = 50$. The graph of this equation is a boundary line that divides the coordinate plane into two parts. One of these parts, along with the boundary line, represents the solution set of the inequality. To determine which part is the solution set, choose a test point that is not on the line. Check to see if the point satisfies the inequality. If it satisfies the inequality, shade the part of the coordinate plane that contains the point. If it doesn't satisfy the inequality, shade the part that does not contain the point.

Example: Graph $y + 2x \leq 50$

Begin by graphing $y + 2x = 50$.

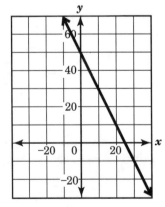

Test a point that is not on the line. The point $(0, 0)$ is a good test point because the numbers are easy to work with, but you may choose any point to test.

$$y + 2x \leq 50$$

$$0 + 2(0) \overset{?}{\leq} 50$$

$$0 + 0 \overset{?}{\leq} 50$$

$$0 \overset{?}{\leq} 50$$

This statement is true, so shade the part of the graph that contains $(0, 0)$.

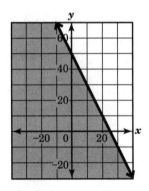

The shaded portion represents the solution set.

When an inequality contains the symbol $<$ or $>$, the boundary line is not part of the solution set. In this case, draw the boundary with a dashed line rather than a solid line.

Example: Graph $y < -x - 1$

Begin by graphing $y = -x - 1$. Use a dashed line, because this line is not part of the solution set.

Test a point that is not on the line. You can use $(0, 0)$.

$$y \overset{?}{<} -x - 1$$
$$0 \overset{?}{<} -(0) - 1$$
$$0 \overset{?}{<} -1$$

Shade the part of the graph that does <u>not</u> contain $(0, 0)$.

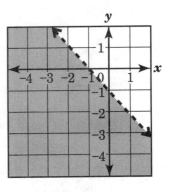

The solution set of a system of inequalities is the set of all ordered pairs that satisfy both inequalities. To graph the solution set of the system, graph the solution sets of both inequalities on the same coordinate system. The intersection of the two graphs is the graph of the solution set of the system. The intersection is the portion of the coordinate plane that is shaded twice.

Example: Graph the system of inequalities. $\quad x - y > 5$
$$x + y \geq -1$$

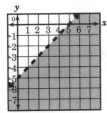 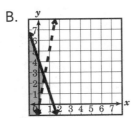 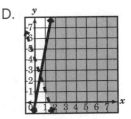

Graph the first inequality. Remember to use a dashed line.

Graph the second inequality on the same plane.

The solution set is the intersection of the graphs.

Self-Test

Circle the letter of the correct answer.

Graph the system of inequalities.

$y \leq 5x$
$3x + y > 4$

A. 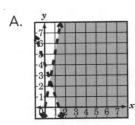 B. 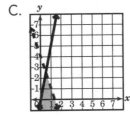 C. 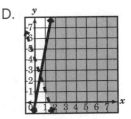 D.

Check your answer.

> D is correct. Graph both inequalities on the same plane. The intersection of the graphs is the graph of the system.

Practice

Solving Systems of Linear Equations

Circle the letter of the correct answer.

1. Graph. $y < x + 1$

A.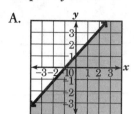

C.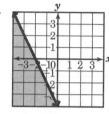

B.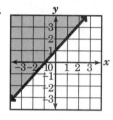

D.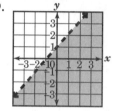

2. Match the graph with the inequality it represents.

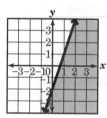

A. $y < 3x - 2$ C. $y > 3x - 2$
B. $y \geq 3x - 2$ D. $y \leq 3x - 2$

3. Match the graph with the inequality it represents.

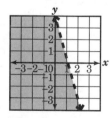

A. $y + 4x \geq 4$ C. $y + 4x < 4$
B. $y + 4x > 4$ D. $y + 4x \leq 4$

4. Graph. $4x + 2y \leq -8$

A.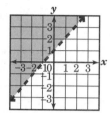

C.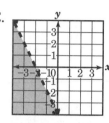

B.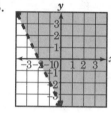

D.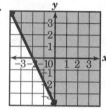

5. Graph. $x - y \geq 4$

A.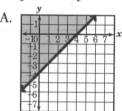

C.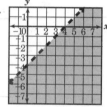

B.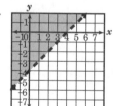

D.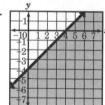

6. Match the graph with the inequality it represents.

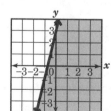

A. $12x - 3y \geq -9$
B. $12x - 3y < -9$
C. $12x - 3y \leq -9$
D. $12x - 3y > -9$

Lesson 31: Solving Systems of Linear Inequalities

7. Graph. $y \leq \frac{2}{3}x + 4$

A.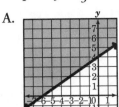

C.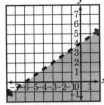

B.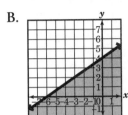

D.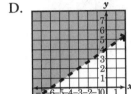

8. Which region represents the solution to the system of inequalities?

$y < 2x + 1$

$y > -x - 1$

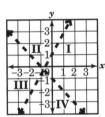

A. I

B. II

C. III

D. IV

9. Match the graph with the inequality it represents.

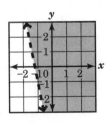

A. $y > -5x - 6$

B. $y \geq -5x - 6$

C. $y \leq -5x - 6$

D. $y < -5x - 6$

10. Solve the system of inequalities by graphing.

$y \geq x + 3$

$y \leq 5 - x$

A.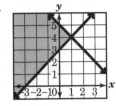

C.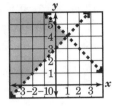

B.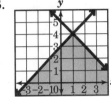

D.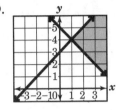

11. This graph represents the solution to which of the following systems of inequalities?

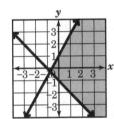

A. $y \leq 2x + 1$
    $y \leq -x - 1$

B. $y > 2x + 1$
    $y > -x - 1$

C. $y \leq 2x + 1$
    $y \geq -x - 1$

D. $y < 2x + 1$
    $y > -x - 1$

12. Solve the system of inequalities by graphing.

$x - 2y \geq 2$

$x + y \geq -2$

A.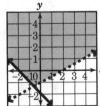

C.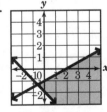

B.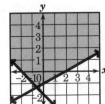

D.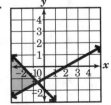

Solving Problems with Systems of Linear Equations

LESSON 32

You will learn how to:
- use systems of equations to solve mixture and investment problems

To solve mixture and investment problems, follow these steps:

1. Define the variables.

2. Use the variables to write equations to represent the given information.

3. Solve the system of equations for both variables.

Example: One brand of candy costs $1.80 per pound. Another brand costs $2.00 per pound. Tifani wants to mix the two brands to form a 5-pound box of candy that will cost $9.40. How many pounds of each type of candy should she use?

1. *Define the variables:* $x =$ the number of pounds of the $1.80/pound candy
$y =$ the number of pounds of the $2.00/pound candy

2. *Write the equations:* $x + y = 5$ The total weight is five pounds.
$1.8x + 2y = 9.4$ The total cost is $9.40.

3. *Solve the system:* $y = 5 - x$ $1.8x + 2(5 - x) = 9.4$ $3 + y = 5$
$x = 3$ $y = 2$

Tifani should use 3 pounds of the $1.80/pound candy and 2 pounds of the $2.00/pound candy.

If a problem includes percents, remember to convert the percents to decimals.

Example: A chemist wants to mix a 50% acid solution with a 75% acid solution to produce 100 milliliters of a 60% acid solution. How many milliliters of each solution are needed?

1. *Define the variables:* $x =$ the number of milliliters of the 50% solution
$y =$ the number of milliliters of the 75% solution

2. *Write the equations:* $x + y = 100$ The total volume is 100 milliliters.
$0.5x + 0.75y = 0.6(100)$ The acidity of the final mixture is 60%.

3. *Solve the system:* $y = 100 - x$ $0.5x + 0.75(100 - x) = 0.6(100)$ $y = 100 - 60$
$x = 60$ $y = 40$

The chemist should use 60 milliliters of the 50% solution and 40 milliliters of the 75% solution.

Investment problems can also be solved using systems of equations.

Example: Rick invested a total of $6,000. He invested part of the money in an account that earned 4% simple interest and the remainder in an account that earned 6% simple interest. His earnings from both accounts totaled $312. How much did he invest in each account?

1. *Define the variables:* x = the number of dollars invested at 4%
y = the number of dollars invested at 6%

2. *Write the equations:* $x + y = 6000$
$0.04x + 0.06y = 312$

3. *Solve the system:* $y = 6000 - x$ $0.04x + 0.06(6000 - x) = 312$ $y = 6000 - 2400$
$x = 2400$ $y = 3600$

He invested $2,400 at 4% and $3,600 at 6%.

Self-Test

Circle the letter of the correct answer.

Kira split $13,000 between two investments, one paying 5% annually and one paying 8% annually. After one year, the amounts of interest from the two investments were equal. How much did she invest at 5%?

A. $3,000

C. $8,000

B. $5,000

D. $10,000

Check your answer.

C is correct.

x = *amount invested at 5%* $x + y = 13{,}000$ $y = 13{,}000 - x$
y = *amount invested at 8%* $0.05x = 0.08y$ $0.05x = 0.08(13{,}000 - x)$
$x = 8{,}000$

Practice

Solving Problems with Systems of Linear Equations

Circle the letter of the correct answer.

1. Inez paid $22.50 for 8 burgers for her friends. Some were hamburgers and some were cheeseburgers. If hamburgers cost $2.50 and cheeseburgers cost $3.00, how many cheeseburgers did Inez buy?

   A. 3
   B. 4
   C. 5
   D. 6

2. The cost of one notebook and one pencil at the school store is $1.45. Four notebooks cost the same amount as 25 pencils. What is the cost of one notebook?

   A. $0.20
   B. $0.25
   C. $1.00
   D. $1.25

3. James wants to mix a 40% acid solution with a 60% acid solution to produce 10 liters of a 50% acid solution. How many liters of the 40% solution does he need?

   A. 3
   B. 4
   C. 5
   D. 6

4. Lelani will use two types of tiles to create a mosaic. The larger tiles cost $0.75 each, and the smaller ones cost $0.50 each. She will use 250 tiles and pay $145. How many small tiles will she use?

   A. 80
   B. 90
   C. 125
   D. 170

5. Josh ordered 125 T-shirts for his family reunion. Adult shirts were $5 each, and children's shirts were $3 each. He paid $535 for the shirts. How many adult shirts did he order?

   A. 45
   B. 80
   C. 96
   D. 102

6. Dave invested a total of $2,000. He invested part of it in an account that earned 4% simple interest and the rest of it in an account that earned 5% simple interest. He earned $91.50 from both accounts. How much did he invest at 4%?

   A. $500
   B. $775
   C. $850
   D. $1,150

7. Principal King bought 6.5 pounds of apples for $8.50 to give to her teachers. The Granny Smith apples were $1.50 per pound and the Red Delicious apples were $1.00 per pound. How many pounds of Red Delicious apples did she buy?

   A. 2.5
   B. 4
   C. 4.75
   D. 6

8. Anna invested $30,000 in two different accounts. One account earned 5% simple interest, and the other earned 9% simple interest. She earned $1,820 from both accounts. How much did she invest at 5%?

    A. $5,000
    B. $8,000
    C. $22,000
    D. $25,000

9. Twelve members of the Lee family paid $360 for admission to an amusement park. Adult tickets were $35 each and children's tickets were $20 each. How many children's tickets did the Lee family buy?

    A. 4
    B. 6
    C. 8
    D. 10

10. A chemist wants to mix a 30% acid solution with a 75% acid solution to produce 2,000 milliliters of a 34.5% acid solution. How many milliliters of the 30% solution does he need?

    A. 200
    B. 450
    C. 1,550
    D. 1,800

11. The yearbook staff has two boxes of photographs. In box 1, 25% of the photos are black and white, and in box 2, 40% of the photos are black and white. When the boxes are combined together, there are 1,000 photographs with 29.5% of them being black and white. How many photos are in box 1?

    A. 300
    B. 450
    C. 550
    D. 700

12. One type of coffee costs $3.75 per pound. Another type costs $15 per pound. Marvin wants to mix the two types to make a 25-pound mixture of coffee worth $150. How many pounds of the $3.75 per pound coffee should he use?

    A. 5
    B. 10
    C. 20
    D. 25

13. 45% of the students in Mr. Knight's class are girls. 60% of the students in Mrs. Black's class are girls. When the two classes combine there are 100 students and 48% of them are girls. How many students are in Mrs. Black's class?

    A. 20
    B. 40
    C. 60
    D. 80

14. Zandra invested $1,500 in two different accounts. One account earned 4.2% simple interest. The other earned 6.4% simple interest. Her earnings from both accounts combined amounted to $87.20. How much did she invest at 4.2%?

    A. $400
    B. $700
    C. $800
    D. $1,100

Graphing Nonlinear Equations

LESSON 33

You will learn how to:

• graph equations of the form $y = nx^2$ and $y = nx^3$

Key Words: parabola, vertex

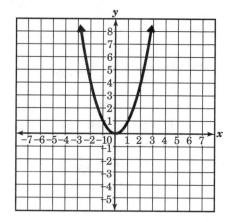

The graph of an equation written in the form $y = nx^2$ is a U-shaped curve called a *parabola*. The curve on the right is the graph of $y = x^2$. The value of n is 1 for this parabola.

The coefficient n determines the direction in which the parabola opens. If n is positive, the parabola opens up. If n is negative, the parabola opens down. The graph shown above opens up because the value of n is positive.

The absolute value of n determines the width of the parabola. Equations with greater values of $|n|$ have narrower parabolas.

Example: Match each equation with its graph.

I. $y = 2x^2$ II. $y = -\frac{2}{3}x^2$ III. $y = 4x^2$ IV. $y = -x^2$

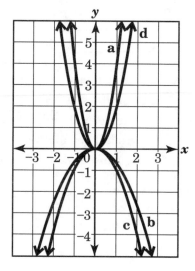

In equations I and III, n is positive, so the graphs of these equations are parabolas that open up. Because the value of $|n|$ is greater in equation III than in equation I, the graph of equation III is narrower than the graph of equation I. Parabolas **a** and **d** both open up, and **a** is narrower than **d**. Therefore, **a** is the graph of equation III, and **d** is the graph of equation I.

In equations II and IV, n is negative, so the graphs of these equations are parabolas that open down. Because the value of $|n|$ is greater in equation IV than in equation II, the graph of equation IV is narrower than the graph of equation II. Parabolas **c** and **b** both open down, and **c** is narrower than **b**. Therefore, **c** is the graph of equation IV, and **b** is the graph of equation II.

The *vertex* of a parabola that opens down is the highest point of the parabola. The vertex of a parabola that opens up is the lowest point of the parabola. For an equation in the form $y = nx^2$, the vertex of its graph is (0, 0). To graph an equation in the form $y = nx^2$, create a table of x-values, find their corresponding y-values, and plot the points that have these coordinates. Include (0, 0) in your table of values. Connect the points to form the parabola.

Example: Graph $y = \frac{1}{2}x^2$.
The equation is in the form
$y = nx^2$. The graph of the
equation is a parabola whose
vertex is $(0, 0)$.

x	y
-2	2
-1	$\frac{1}{2}$
0	0
1	$\frac{1}{2}$
2	2

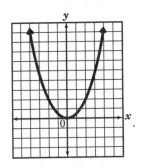

The graph of an equation written in the form $y = nx^3$ is an
S-shaped curve. The figure on the right is the graph of $y = x^3$.

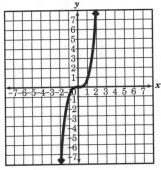

The value of n determines the quadrants that contain the graph.
If n is positive, the graph is in quadrants I and III. If n is negative,
the graph is in quadrants II and IV.

The absolute value of n determines the width of the graph. Greater
values of $|n|$ will create narrower graphs.

Example: Match each equation with its graph.

     F. $y = -x^3$ G. $y = 3x^3$ H. $y = \frac{1}{2}x^3$

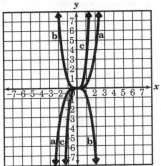

Only equation F has a negative value for n, so it matches the graph
that is in quadrants II and IV. The graph of equation F is **b**. The
graphs of equations G and H are in quadrants I and III. Because
$|n|$ is greater for equation G than for equation H, the graph of
equation G is narrower. The graph of equation H is **a**, and the
graph of equation G is **c**.

To graph an equation written in the form $y = nx^3$, create a table of
values. Then plot the point $(0, 0)$ and several points on either side
of $(0, 0)$. Draw an S-shaped curve through the points.

Self-Test

Circle the letter of the correct answer.

Match the equation with the description of its graph. $y = -8x^2$

A. parabola, opens up, narrower than $y = x^2$
B. parabola, opens down, wider than $y = x^2$
C. parabola, opens up, wider than $y = x^2$
D. parabola, opens down, narrower than $y = x^2$

Check your answer.

    D is correct.

    *n is negative, so the parabola opens down. The absolute
value of n is greater than 1, so the graph is narrower than
the graph of $y = x^2$.*

Lesson 33: Graphing Nonlinear Equations

Practice

Graphing Nonlinear Equations

Circle the letter of the correct answer.

1. Which equation matches the graph?

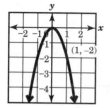

A. $y = x^2$
B. $y = 2x^2$
C. $y = -2x^2$
D. $y = -x^2$

2. Which of the following could be the equation that matches the given graph?

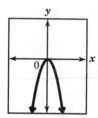

A. $y = 7x^2$
B. $y = -7x^2$
C. $y = 7x^3$
D. $y = -7x^3$

3. Graph $y = 2x^3$.

A. 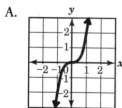 C.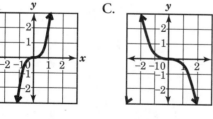

B. 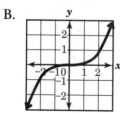 D.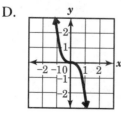

4. Which equation matches the graph?

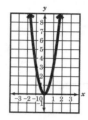

A. $y = 3x^2$
B. $y = -3x^2$
C. $y = \frac{1}{3}x^2$
D. $y = -\frac{1}{3}x^2$

5. Graph $y = -\frac{2}{3}x^2$.

A. 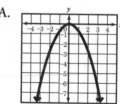 C.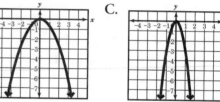

B. 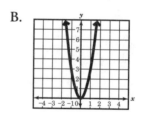 D.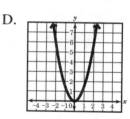

6. Which equation matches the graph?

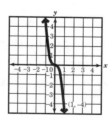

A. $y = 4x^3$
B. $y = x^3$
C. $y = -x^3$
D. $y = -4x^3$

Lesson 33: Graphing Nonlinear Equations

7. Which of the following could be the equation that matches the given graph?

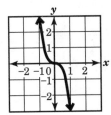

A. $y = 3x^2$

B. $y = -3x^2$

C. $y = 3x^3$

D. $y = -3x^3$

8. Graph $y = -\frac{3}{4}x^3$.

A.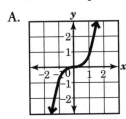

C.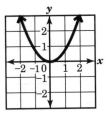

B.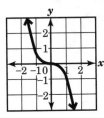

D.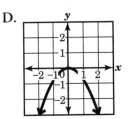

9. Match the equation with the description of its graph.

$y = -8x^2$

A. parabola, opens up, narrower than $y = x^2$

B. parabola, opens down, narrower than $y = x^2$

C. parabola, opens up, wider than $y = x^2$

D. parabola, opens down, wider than $y = x^2$

10. Which equation matches the graph?

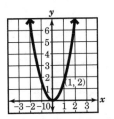

A. $y = -10x^2$

B. $y = 5x^2$

C. $y = -5x^2$

D. $y = 10x^2$

11. Match the equation with the description of its graph.

$y = \frac{1}{6}x^2$

A. parabola, opens up, narrower than $y = x^2$

B. parabola, opens down, narrower than $y = x^2$

C. parabola, opens up, wider than $y = x^2$

D. parabola, opens down, wider than $y = x^2$

12. Which equation matches the graph?

A. $y = 2x^3$

B. $y = -2x^3$

C. $y = 2x^2$

D. $y = -x^2$

Comparing and Converting Units of Measurement

LESSON 34

You will learn how to:

- compare weights, capacities, geometric measures, times, and temperatures within and between systems

Key Words: customary system, metric system

In the United States, the *customary system* is used to measure length, weight, capacity, and temperature. In most other countries, the *metric system* is used.

The table shows relationships for some units in the customary system.

Length	Weight	Capacity
1 foot (ft) = 12 inches (in.) 1 yard (yd) = 3 ft 1 mile (mi) = 5,280 ft	1 pound (lb) = 16 ounces (oz) 1 ton (T) = 2,000 lb	1 cup (c) = 8 fluid ounces (fl oz) 1 pint (pt) = 2 c 1 quart (qt) = 2 pt 1 gallon (gal) = 4 qt

In general, to change from a larger unit to a smaller unit, multiply. To change from a smaller unit to a larger unit, divide.

Examples:	Method			Solution
5 ft = _____ in.	larger unit 1 ft = 12 in.	→	smaller unit Multiply by 12.	$5 \cdot 12 = 60$ 5 ft = 60 in.
40 oz = _____ lb	smaller unit 16 oz = 1 lb	→	larger unit Divide by 16.	$40 \div 16 = 2.5$ 40 oz = 2.5 lb

In metric measurement, the prefix in the name of a unit tells how that unit compares to the basic unit: milli means one thousandth, centi means one hundredth, and kilo means one thousand.

Length – meter (m)	Weight – gram (g)	Capacity – liter (L)
1 meter (m) = 1,000 millimeters (mm) 1 meter (m) = 100 centimeters (cm) 1 kilometer (km) = 1,000 meters (m)	1 gram (g) = 1,000 milligrams (mg) 1 kilogram (kg) = 1,000 grams (g)	1 liter (L) = 1,000 milliliters (mL)

Examples:	Method			Solution
560 cm = _____ m	smaller unit 1 m = 100 cm	→	larger unit Divide by 100.	$560 \div 100 = 5.6$ 560 cm = 5.6 m
4.5 kg = _____ g	larger unit 1 kg = 1,000 g	→	smaller unit Multiply by 1,000.	$4.5 \cdot 1,000 = 4,500$ 4.5 kg = 4,500 g

Sometimes it is necessary to convert between the customary and metric systems. The table shows some approximations to use.

Length	Weight	Capacity
1 in. ≈ 2.54 cm 1 mi. ≈ 1.6 km	1 oz ≈ 28 g 1 kg ≈ 2.2 lb	1 L ≈ 1.06 qt

Examples:	Method			Solution
8 in. ≈ ___ cm	larger unit 1 in. ≈ 2.54 cm	→	smaller unit Multiply by 2.54.	8 · 2.54 ≈ 20.32 8 in. ≈ 20.32 cm
210 g ≈ ___ oz	smaller unit 1 oz ≈ 28 g	→	larger unit Divide by 28.	210 ÷ 28 ≈ 7.5 210 g ≈ 7.5 oz
3.5 L ≈ ___ qt	larger unit 1 L ≈ 1.06 qt	→	smaller unit Multiply by 1.06.	3.5 · 1.06 ≈ 3.71 3.5 L ≈ 3.71 qt

In the U.S., temperature is measured on the Fahrenheit scale (°F). In the metric system, temperature is measured on the Celsius scale (°C). The table gives a comparison of some familiar temperatures on both scales.

Situation	Fahrenheit Temperature	Celsius Temperature
Water freezes	32°F	0°C
Room temperature	68°F	20°C
Normal body temperature	98.6°F	37°C
Water boils	212°F	100°C

Example: Choose the more reasonable temperature.

A warm day: 30°C or 30°F
30°C is more than normal room temperature.
30°F is close to the freezing point.
So, 30°C is a more reasonable temperature for a warm day.

A bowl of hot soup: 190°F or 190°C
190°C is much higher than the boiling point of water. 190°F is just below the boiling point of water. So, 190°F is a more reasonable temperature for a bowl of hot soup.

Self-Test

Circle the letter of the correct answer.

The height of a ceiling is 8 ft. How many yards is this?

A. $\frac{3}{2}$ yd   B. $\frac{8}{3}$ yd   C. 24 yd   D. 96 yd

Check your answer.

B is correct.

Divide to convert from a smaller unit to a larger unit.

$8 ÷ 3 = \frac{8}{3}$

Practice

Comparing and Converting Units of Measurement

Circle the letter of the correct answer.

1. Mayra is 66 inches tall. What is her height in feet? (1 foot = 12 inches)

A. 5 ft

B. 5.5 ft

C. 6 ft

D. 6.6 ft

2. One of the highest mountains in California is White Mt. Peak. It is 14,256 feet tall. About how many miles is this? (1 mile = 5,280 feet)

A. 2.7 mi

B. 8.1 mi

C. 396 mi

D. 1,188 mi

3. An African elephant can reach a weight of 15,400 pounds. How many tons is this? (1 ton = 2,000 pounds)

A. 7.7

B. 77

C. 770

D. 30,800

4. Mrs. Blake bought 2.5 pounds of chicken. How many ounces did she buy? (1 pound = 16 ounces)

A. 18.5 oz

B. 25 oz

C. 32.5 oz

D. 40 oz

5. A recipe calls for 12 fl oz of water. How many cups of water are needed? (1 cup = 8 fluid ounces)

A. $1\frac{1}{4}$

B. $1\frac{1}{2}$

C. $1\frac{3}{4}$

D. $2\frac{1}{4}$

6. A chef prepares 5 gallons of soup at a time. How many quarts of soup is this? (1 gallon = 4 quarts)

A. $1\frac{1}{4}$ qt

B. 9 qt

C. 10 qt

D. 20 qt

7. The ears of an African elephant may reach a length of 1.5 meters from top to bottom. How many centimeters is this? (1 meter = 100 centimeters)

A. 15 cm

B. 150 cm

C. 1,500 cm

D. 15,000 cm

8. A dollar bill is about 65 millimeters wide. What is the width of a dollar bill in meters? (1 meter = 1,000 millimeters)

A. 0.065

B. 0.65

C. 6.5

D. 65,000

Lesson 34: Comparing and Converting Units of Measurement

9. How many centimeters long is a 12-inch ruler? (1 inch ≈ 2.54 centimeters)

A. 4.8 cm
B. 14.54 cm
C. 24 cm
D. 30.48 cm

10. The approximate driving distance from San Francisco, California, to Vancouver, British Columbia, is 954 miles. What is the approximate driving distance in kilometers? (1 mile ≈ 1.6 kilometers)

A. 596 km
B. 1,049 km
C. 1,526 km
D. 1,908 km

11. Larry weighs 143 pounds. What is his weight in kilograms? (1 kilogram ≈ 2.2 pounds)

A. 2.2
B. 65
C. 71.5
D. 314.6

12. Louise bought 16 liters of soda for a party. About how many quarts of soda did she buy? (1 liter ≈ 1.06 quarts)

A. 8 qt
B. 15 qt
C. 16 qt
D. 17 qt

13. A can of chicken noodle soup has a net weight of 301 grams. What is its net weight in ounces? (1 ounce ≈ 28 grams)

A. $10\frac{3}{4}$ oz
B. $107\frac{1}{2}$ oz
C. 1,075 oz
D. 8,428 oz

14. Which temperature is most reasonable for the inside of a freezer?

A. 0°C
B. 5°C
C. 10°F
D. 40°F

15. Which temperature is most reasonable for a cool spring day?

A. 15°C
B. 15°F
C. 30°F
D. 30°C

16. Which temperature is most reasonable to bake a cake?

A. 20°C
B. 50°C
C. 100°F
D. 350°F

17. How many days are there in 168 hours? (1 day = 24 hours)

A. 2.8
B 3.2
C. 7
D. 14

18. How many minutes are in $2\frac{1}{4}$ hours? (1 hour = 60 minutes)

A. 125 minutes
B. 130 minutes
C. 135 minutes
D. 225 minutes

Comparing and Converting Square and Cubic Units of Measurement

LESSON 35

You will learn how to:

• convert area and volume measures within and between measurement systems

Key Words: area, square unit, volume, cubic unit

The *area* of a flat object is a measure of the surface it covers, or the surface inside of it. Area is expressed in *square units*. The rectangle has an area of 10 square centimeters, or 10 cm², because it takes 10 squares with each side 1 cm long to cover the rectangle.

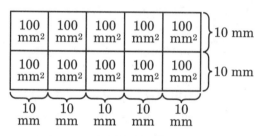

Area = 10 cm²

The area of the same rectangle can also be expressed in square millimeters, or mm². Because there are 10 mm in each cm, the area of each cm² is 100 mm². That is, 1 cm² = 100 mm². Therefore, the area of the same rectangle is (10 × 100) mm², or 1,000 mm².

Area = 1,000 mm²

The table shows the relationships for some common units of area measure.

Customary System	Equivalents between Systems	Metric System
1 ft² = 144 in.² 1 yd² = 9 ft²	1 in.² ≈ 6.45 cm²	1 cm² = 100 mm² 1 m² = 10,000 cm²

Remember to multiply when converting to smaller units of measure and to divide when converting to larger units of measure.

Examples:	Method		Solution
135 ft² = _____ yd²	smaller unit 1 yd² = 9 ft²	→ larger unit Divide by 9.	135 ÷ 9 = 15 135 ft² = 15 yd²
4 m² = _____ cm²	larger unit 1 m² = 10,000 cm²	→ smaller unit Multiply by 10,000.	4 · 10,000 = 40,000 4 m² = 40,000 cm²
9 in.² ≈ _____ cm²	larger unit 1 in.² ≈ 6.45 cm²	→ smaller unit Multiply by 6.45.	9 · 6.45 = 58.05 9 in.² ≈ 58.05 cm²

The *volume* of a three-dimensional object is a measure of the space it occupies, or the space inside of it. Volume is expressed in **cubic units.** The cube has a volume of 1 cubic yard, or 1 yd³, because it measures 1 yd on each edge.

The volume of the same cube can also be expressed in cubic feet, or ft³. The cube measures 3 ft on each edge because 1 yd = 3 ft. Therefore, the cube has a volume of (3 × 3 × 3) ft³, or 27 ft³.

The table shows the relationships for some common units of volume measure.

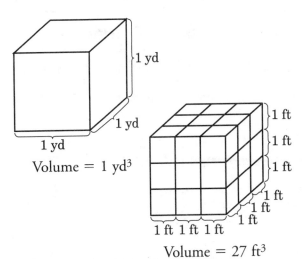

Volume = 1 yd³

Volume = 27 ft³

Customary System	Equivalents between Systems	Metric System
1 ft³ = 1,728 in.³ 1 yd³ = 27 ft³	1 in.³ ≈ 16.38 cm³	1 cm³ = 1,000 mm³ 1 m³ = 1,000,000 cm³ 1 L = 1,000 mL = 1,000 cm³

Examples:	Method	Solution
81 ft³ = _____ yd³	smaller unit → larger unit 1 yd³ = 27 ft³ Divide by 27.	81 ÷ 27 = 3 81 ft³ = 3 yd³
7 cm³ = _____ mm³	larger unit → smaller unit 1 cm³ = 1,000 mm³ Multiply by 1,000.	7 · 1,000 = 7,000 7 cm³ = 7,000 mm³
10 in.³ ≈ _____ cm³	larger unit → smaller unit 1 in.³ ≈ 16.38 cm³ Multiply by 16.38.	10 · 16.38 = 163.8 10 in.³ ≈ 163.8 cm³

Self-Test
Circle the letter of the correct answer.

1. How many square feet are in 9 square yards?

   A. 18   C. 81

   B. 27   D. 324

2. How many cubic centimeters are in 50,000 cubic millimeters?

   A.   5   C. 500

   B. 50   D. 5,000

Check your answer.

C is correct.

Multiply to convert from a larger unit to a smaller unit.

9 · 9 = 81

B is correct.

Divide to convert from a smaller unit to a larger unit.

50,000 ÷ 1,000 = 50

Practice

Comparing and Computing Square and Cubic Units of Measurement

Circle the letter of the correct answer.

1. How many square inches are in 3 square feet?

   A. 36
   B. 144
   C. 432
   D. 1,296

2. How many square feet are in 360 square inches?

   A. 2.5
   B. 3
   C. 25
   D. 30

3. How many square yards are in 108 square feet?

   A. 9
   B. 12
   C. 24
   D. 36

4. How many square feet are in 4 square yards?

   A. 16
   B. 24
   C. 36
   D. 48

5. About how many square centimeters are equivalent to 30 square inches?

   A. 4.65
   B. 75
   C. 76.2
   D. 193.5

6. How many square centimeters are in 1,500 square millimeters?

   A. 1.5
   B. 15
   C. 150
   D. 150,000

7. How many square millimeters are in 6.1 square centimeters?

   A. 601
   B. 610
   C. 6,010
   D. 6,100

8. How many square meters are in 2,500 square centimeters?

   A. 0.25
   B. 2.5
   C. 25
   D. 250

9. How many square centimeters are in 30 square meters?

   A. 0.003
   B. 0.3
   C. 3,000
   D. 300,000

10. How many cubic inches are in 7.5 cubic feet?

   A. 90
   B. 230.4
   C. 12,096
   D. 12,960

Lesson 35: Comparing and Converting Square and Cubic Units of Measurement

11. How many cubic feet are in 10,800 cubic inches?

A. 6.25
B. 62.5
C. 75
D. 900

12. How many cubic yards are in 216 cubic feet?

A. 8
B. 9
C. 24
D. 72

13. How many cubic feet are in $9\frac{1}{3}$ cubic yards?

A. 243
B. 252
C. 261
D. 270

14. About how many cubic centimeters are equivalent to 5 cubic inches?

A. 3.276
B. 12.7
C. 32.25
D. 81.9

15. How many cubic millimeters are in 14 cubic centimeters?

A. 140
B. 1,400
C. 14,000
D. 140,000

16. How many cubic centimeters are in 450 cubic millimeters?

A. 0.045
B. 0.45
C. 4.5
D. 45

17. How many cubic meters are in 10,000,000 cubic centimeters?

A. 1
B. 10
C. 100
D. 1,000

18. How many cubic centimeters are in 0.9 cubic meters?

A. 9,000
B. 90,000
C. 900,000
D. 9,000,000

19. How many cubic centimeters are there in 4 liters?

A. 4
B. 40
C. 400
D. 4,000

20. How many milliliters are there in 200 cubic centimeters?

A. 0.2
B. 2
C. 20
D. 200

Comparing and Converting Rates

LESSON 36

You will learn how to:
- solve problems involving rates and products
- check answers for reasonableness and correct units

Key Words: rate, unit rate

A ratio is a comparison of two numbers by division. A *rate* is a ratio that compares two quantities expressed in different units of measure, like miles with gallons, or cents with ounces. If a car travels 100 miles on 5 gallons of gas, then its rate of gasoline consumption is $\frac{100 \text{ miles}}{5 \text{ gallons}} = \frac{20 \text{ miles}}{1 \text{ gallon}} = 20$ miles per gallon. 20 miles per gallon is a unit rate. A *unit rate* is a rate in which the denominator is 1.

Examples: Express each as a unit rate.

Description	Rate	Unit Rate
A car travels 200 miles in 4 hours.	$\frac{200 \text{ miles}}{4 \text{ hours}} = \frac{50 \text{ miles}}{1 \text{ hour}}$	50 miles per hour
The weight of 3 cubic feet of water is 192 pounds.	$\frac{192 \text{ pounds}}{3 \text{ cubic feet}} = \frac{64 \text{ pounds}}{1 \text{ cubic foot}}$	64 pounds per cubic foot

To convert a rate to a rate containing a different unit of measure, multiply by the appropriate conversion factor. The conversion factor must be a fraction that compares the given unit of measure with the new (different) unit of measure.

Example: Convert 20 m/s to m/min.

$\frac{20 \text{ m}}{1 \text{ s}} = \frac{? \text{ m}}{1 \text{ min}}$

Write the given rate and the unknown rate in fraction form. The given unit of measure is seconds and the new unit of measure is minutes.

Conversion factor: $\frac{60 \text{ s}}{1 \text{ min}}$

The conversion factor must contain seconds and minutes. Because there are 60 seconds in a minute, the conversion factor is $\frac{60 \text{ s}}{1 \text{ min}}$.

$\frac{20 \text{ m}}{\cancel{s}} \cdot \frac{60 \cancel{s}}{1 \text{ min}} = \frac{1,200 \text{ m}}{1 \text{ min}}$

Multiply and cancel any unit that appears in both a numerator and a denominator.

$20 \text{ m/s} = 1,200 \text{ m/min}$

This answer is reasonable because a moving object can go 60 times as far in one minute as in one second.

Example: Convert 5 oz/min to g/min. (1 oz ≈ 28 g)

$\frac{5 \text{ oz}}{1 \text{ min}} = \frac{? \text{ g}}{1 \text{ min}}$

Write the given rate and the unknown rate in fraction form. The given unit of measure is ounces and the new unit of measure is grams.

Conversion factor: $\frac{28 \text{ g}}{1 \text{ oz}}$

The conversion factor must contain ounces and grams. Because there are about 28 grams in an ounce, the conversion factor is $\frac{28 \text{ g}}{1 \text{ oz}}$.

$\frac{5 \cancel{\text{oz}}}{1 \text{ min}} \cdot \frac{28 \text{ g}}{1 \cancel{\text{oz}}} \approx \frac{140 \text{ g}}{1 \text{ min}}$

Multiply and cancel as needed.

$5 \text{ oz/min} \approx 140 \text{ g/min}$

Example: Convert 1,000 yd/hr to ft/min.

$$\frac{1,000 \text{ yd}}{1 \text{ hr}} = \frac{? \text{ ft}}{1 \text{ min}}$$

Write the given rate and the unknown rate in fraction form. The given units of measure are yd and hr and the new (different) units of measure are ft and min.

Conversion factors: $\frac{3 \text{ ft}}{1 \text{ yd}}$ and $\frac{1 \text{ hr}}{60 \text{ min}}$

One conversion factor must contain yd and ft, and the other conversion factor must contain hr and min. Use $\frac{3 \text{ ft}}{1 \text{ yd}}$ and $\frac{1 \text{ hr}}{60 \text{ min}}$.

$$\frac{1,000 \text{ yd}}{1 \text{ hr}} \cdot \frac{3 \text{ ft}}{1 \text{ yd}} \cdot \frac{1 \text{ hr}}{60 \text{ min}} = \frac{3,000 \text{ ft}}{60 \text{ min}} = \frac{50 \text{ ft}}{1 \text{ min}}$$ Multiply and cancel as needed.

1,000 yd/hr = 50 ft/min

Example: If it takes 3 days for 2 workers to paint a house, how long will it take 4 workers, working at the same rate, to paint the house?

If 2 workers can paint the house in 3 days, then 2 · 3, or 6, worker-days are required to paint the house. To find how long it will take 4 workers, divide.

$$\frac{6 \text{ worker-days}}{4 \text{ workers}} = 1.5 \text{ days}$$

It will take 4 workers 1.5 days to paint the house.

Self-Test

Circle the letter of the correct answer.

1. Order the following three speeds from fastest to slowest: 4 ft/s, 180 ft/min, 100 yd/min.

   A. 180 ft/min   100 yd/min   4 ft/s
   B. 100 yd/min   4 ft/s   180 ft/min
   C. 4 ft/s   100 yd/min   180 ft/min
   D. 100 yd/min   180 ft/min   4 ft/s

2. It takes 8 hours for 2 men to plant a hedge. At the same rate, how long will it take 4 men?

   A. 2 hours
   B. 4 hours
   C. 6 hours
   D. 16 hours

Check your answer.

B is correct.

$$\frac{4 \text{ ft}}{1 \text{ s}} = \frac{4 \text{ ft}}{1 \text{ s}} \cdot \frac{60 \text{ s}}{1 \text{ min}} = \frac{240 \text{ ft}}{1 \text{ min}}$$

$$\frac{100 \text{ yd}}{1 \text{ min}} = \frac{100 \text{ yd}}{1 \text{ min}} \cdot \frac{3 \text{ ft}}{1 \text{ yd}} = \frac{300 \text{ ft}}{1 \text{ min}}$$

fastest to slowest:

  300 ft/min,   240 ft/min,   180 ft/min

or: 100 yd/min,   4 ft/s,   180 ft/min

B is correct.
If it takes 2 men 8 hours to plant a hedge, then 2 · 8, or 16, man-hours are required. To find how long it would take 4 men, divide.

$$\frac{16 \text{ man-hours}}{4 \text{ men}} = 4 \text{ hours}$$

Practice

Comparing and Converting Rates

Circle the letter of the correct answer.

1. A train travels 140 miles in 2 hours. What is the train's rate in miles per hour?

   A. 35 miles per hour
   B. 70 miles per hour
   C. 140 miles per hour
   D. 280 miles per hour

2. A 12-oz box of crackers costs $1.92. What is the price per ounce?

   A. $0.12 per ounce
   B. $0.16 per ounce
   C. $0.18 per ounce
   D. $0.19 per ounce

3. May can type 165 words in 3 minutes. What is her typing speed in words per minute?

   A. 45 words per minute
   B. 55 words per minute
   C. 65 words per minute
   D. 495 words per minute

4. If it takes 45 minutes for 3 chefs to prepare salad ingredients, how long will it take 5 chefs, working at the same rate?

   A. 27 minutes
   B. 30 minutes
   C. 40 minutes
   D. 75 minutes

5. If four friends share a hotel room, each will pay $36. How much would it cost each friend if only 3 friends share the room?

   A. $27
   B. $24
   C. $48
   D. $72

6. It takes 6 workers 12 days to complete a project. At the same rate, how long will it take 8 workers to complete the same project?

   A. 9 days
   B. 12 days
   C. 14 days
   D. 24 days

7. Which is an equivalent rate to 35 km/hr expressed in m/hr?

   A. 0.035 m/hr
   B. 350 m/hr
   C. 3,500 m/hr
   D. 35,000 m/hr

8. Which is an equivalent rate to 60 mi/hr expressed in mi/min?

   A. 1 mi/min
   B. 2 mi/min
   C. 3 mi/min
   D. 10 mi/min

9. Convert 120 yd/hr to yd/min.

   A. 2 yd/min
   B. 40 yd/min
   C. 60 yd/min
   D. 120 yd/min

10. Convert 360 in./min to in./s.

    A. 6 in./s
    B. 30 in./s
    C. 60 in./s
    D. 180 in./s

11. Which is an equivalent rate to 5 in./min expressed in cm/min? (1 in. ≈ 2.54 cm)

A. 1.27 cm/min

B. 1.97 cm/min

C. 12.7 cm/min

D. 127 cm/min

12. Which is an equivalent rate to 88 km/hr expressed in mi/hr? (1 km ≈ 0.6 mi)

A. 52.8 mi/hr

B. 66 mi/hr

C. 88.6 mi/hr

D. 146.7 mi/hr

13. Which is an equivalent rate to 8 lb/gal expressed in kg/gal? (1 lb = 0.45 kg)

A. 3.6 kg/gal

B. 4.32 kg/gal

C. 17.8 kg/gal

D. 36 kg/gal

14. Convert 9 ft/s to ft/min.

A. 9 ft/min

B. 54 ft/min

C. 540 ft/min

D. 630 ft/min

15. Convert 100 yd/min to ft/s.

A. 480 ft/s

B. 60 ft/s

C. 1.6 ft/s

D. 5 ft/s

16. Convert 6 m/s to m/hr.

A. 60 m/hr

B. 360 m/hr

C. 2,160 m/hr

D. 21,600 m/hr

17. Convert 6,000 cm/min to m/s.

A. 1 m/s

B. 36 m/s

C. 60 m/s

D. 600 m/s

18. Order the following three speeds from fastest to slowest: 900 yd/hr, 2,400 ft/hr, 42 ft/min.

A. 42 ft/min   900 yd/hr   2,400 ft/hr

B. 2,400 ft/hr   900 yd/hr   42 ft/min

C. 2,400 ft/hr   42 ft/min   900 yd/hr

D. 900 yd/hr   42 ft/min   2,400 ft/hr

19. Order the following three speeds from slowest to fastest: 2 in./s, 15 ft/min, 4 yd/min.

A. 2 in./s   15 ft/min   4 yd/min

B   2 in./s   4 yd/min   15 ft/min

C. 4 yd/min   2 in./s   15 ft/min

D. 15 ft/min   2 in./s   4 yd/min

20. Order the following three speeds from fastest to slowest: 100 mi/hr, 2,000 mi/day, 2 mi/min.

A. 2 mi/min   100 mi/hr   2,000 mi/day

B. 100 mi/hr   2 mi/min   2,000 mi/day

C. 2,000 mi/day   100 mi/hr   2 mi/min

D. 100 mi/hr   2,000 mi/day   2 mi/min

Solving Direct Variation Problems

LESSON 37

You will learn how to:
- solve multistep problems involving direct variation

Key Words: direct variation

Suppose you get paid $6 per hour. Your total pay varies directly with the number of hours that you work.

h (hours)	5	10	15	20
p (pay)	$30	$60	$90	$120

The relationship between the number of hours worked, h, and the pay, p, can be shown by the equation $p = 6h$. This type of equation is called a *direct variation.* If the hourly wage is k, then the equation is $p = kh$.

Example: Mr. Roth earned $84 for 12 hours of work. How much will he earn if he works for 15 hours at the same rate?

First, find his hourly wage.

$$p = kh$$
$$84 = k(12)$$
$$7 = k$$

Hourly wage: $7 per hour

Next, find his earnings for 15 hours at $7 per hour.

$$p = kh$$
$$p = 7(15)$$
$$p = 105$$

Earnings for 15 hours: $105

Mr. Roth will earn $105 if he works 15 hours.

Direct variation problems can also be solved by using proportions.

Example: Two pounds of potatoes cost $1.18. At this price, how much will 5 pounds of potatoes cost?

$$\frac{2 \text{ pounds}}{\$1.18} = \frac{5 \text{ pounds}}{\$x}$$

$$2x = 5.90$$

$$x = 2.95$$

Write a proportion. Be sure the units of measure in the numerators (pounds) are the same, and be sure the units of measure in the denominators (dollars) are the same.
Cross multiply.
Divide to solve for the variable.

Five pounds of potatoes will cost $2.95.

Example: Julie can type 280 words in five minutes. How long will it take her to type 952 words?

$$\frac{280 \text{ words}}{5 \text{ minutes}} = \frac{952 \text{ words}}{x \text{ minutes}}$$

$$280x = 4{,}760$$

$$x = 17$$

Write a proportion. Be sure the units of measure in the numerators (words) are the same, and be sure the units of measure in the denominators (minutes) are the same.
Cross multiply.
Divide to solve for the variable.

Julie can type 952 words in 17 minutes.

Distance, average speed, and time are related by the following formula:

distance = rate · time, or $d = rt$ In this formula, rate is average speed.

Example: Find the distance, average speed, or time.

Find the distance traveled in five hours at an average speed of 40 mph.	Find the average speed if you travel 135 miles in 3 hours.	Find the time it takes to travel 225 miles at an average speed of 50 mph.
$d = rt$ $d = 40 \cdot 5$ $d = 200$ The distance is 200 mi.	$d = rt$ $135 = r \cdot 3$ $45 = r$ The average speed is 45 mph.	$d = rt$ $225 = 50 \cdot t$ $4.5 = t$ The time is 4.5 hours.

The following type of problem can be solved using a proportion instead of the formula.

Example: A bicyclist traveled 12 miles in $1\frac{1}{2}$ hours. At the same rate, how long will it take the bicyclist to ride 56 miles?

$\dfrac{12 \text{ miles}}{1\frac{1}{2} \text{ hours}} = \dfrac{56 \text{ miles}}{x \text{ hours}}$ Write a proportion. Be sure the units of measure in the numerators (miles) are the same, and be sure the units of measure in the denominators (hours) are the same.

$12x = 84$ Cross multiply.
$x = 7$ Divide to solve for the variable.

It will take the bicyclist 7 hours to ride 56 miles.

Self-Test

Circle the letter of the correct answer.

1. Socks are on sale, six pairs for $21. How much will four pairs of socks cost?

   A. $3.50   C. $14.00

   B. $7.00   D. $19.00

2. A bus traveled 110 miles in two hours. At this rate, how far can the bus travel in five hours?

   A. 55 mi   C. 220 mi

   B. 165 mi   D. 275 mi

Check your answer.

1. *C is correct.*

   $\dfrac{6 \text{ pairs}}{\$21} = \dfrac{4 \text{ pairs}}{\$x}$

   $6x = 84$

   $x = 14$

   4 pairs will cost $14.

2. *D is correct.*

   $\dfrac{110 \text{ miles}}{2 \text{ hours}} = \dfrac{x \text{ miles}}{5 \text{ hours}}$

   $550 = 2x$

   $275 = x$

   The bus will travel 275 miles.

Practice

Solving Direct Variation Problems

Circle the letter of the correct answer.

1. Consuelo can read 64 pages in two hours. At this rate, how many pages can she read in seven hours?

   A. 14 pages

   B. 128 pages

   C. 192 pages

   D. 224 pages

2. Gregg can read 84 pages in three hours. At this rate, how long will it take him to read 140 pages?

   A. 5 hours

   B. 8 hours

   C. 15 hours

   D. 28 hours

3. Rob earned $75 in 15 hours. At this rate, how much will he earn in 25 hours?

   A. $85

   B. $100

   C. $125

   D. $175

4. Carly earned $54 mowing six lawns. How many lawns does she have to mow to earn $126?

   A. 9 lawns

   B. 12 lawns

   C. 14 lawns

   D. 15 lawns

5. Three pounds of peaches cost $5.07. At this price, how much will four pounds of peaches cost?

   A. $6.46

   B. $6.56

   C. $6.66

   D. $6.76

6. A 4.5 pound roast is selling for $12.96. How much will a 6.25 pound roast cost?

   A. $17.28

   B. $18.00

   C. $18.72

   D. $19.00

7. There are 108 calories in 9 pretzels. How many calories are in 20 pretzels?

   A. 119

   B. 180

   C. 200

   D. 240

8. A family of four paid $27 for movie tickets. How much would it have cost if only three people went to the movies?

   A. $20.00

   B. $20.25

   C. $20.50

   D. $20.75

9. Laura has 75 shares of a stock which paid a dividend of $18. Rich has 100 shares of the same stock. How much of a dividend should he receive?

   A. $18.25

   B. $22.50

   C. $24.00

   D. $28.00

10. Jordan typed 675 words in 15 minutes. How many words can he type in 20 minutes?

    A. 750 words

    B. 800 words

    C. 900 words

    D. 1,000 words

11. Towels are on sale at two for $9. How many towels can you get for $40.50?

   A. 7

   B. 8

   C. 9

   D. 10

12. A three-pound roast chicken costs $3.87. At this price, how much will a five-pound roast chicken cost?

   A. $6.45

   B. $7.74

   C. $11.61

   D. $19.35

13. Find the distance traveled in three hours at an average speed of 54 mph.

   A.   18 miles

   B.   57 miles

   C. 152 miles

   D. 162 miles

14. Find the average speed if you travel 225 miles in five hours.

   A. 45 mph

   B. 52 mph

   C. 55 mph

   D. 65 mph

15. Find the time it takes to travel 264 miles at an average speed of 48 mph.

   A. 4 hours

   B. 4.5 hours

   C. 5 hours

   D. 5.5 hours

16. A bus traveled 156 miles in three hours. At this rate, how far can the bus travel in four hours?

   A. 160 miles

   B. 200 miles

   C. 208 miles

   D. 224 miles

17. Colleen jogged 18 miles in $4\frac{1}{2}$ hours. At the same rate, how long would it take her to jog 12 miles?

   A. $2\frac{1}{2}$ hours

   B. 3 hours

   C. $3\frac{1}{2}$ hours

   D. 4 hours

18. Paul drove 130 miles at an average speed of 52 mph. If he drives for the same amount of time at an average speed of 48 mph, how many miles will he drive?

   A. 100 miles

   B. 115 miles

   C. 120 miles

   D. 126 miles

19. A train traveled 336 miles in four hours. At this rate, how far can the train travel in six hours?

   A. 400 miles

   B. 420 miles

   C. 504 miles

   D. 672 miles

20. Matt walked three miles in 60 minutes. At the same rate, how long would it take him to walk five miles?

   A. 75 minutes

   B. 80 minutes

   C. 90 minutes

   D. 100 minutes

Interpreting Scale Drawings and Models

LESSON 38

You will learn how to:
• construct and read drawings and models made to scale

Key Words: scale drawing, scale

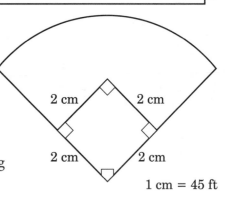

A *scale drawing* shows an object in proportion to its actual measurements. Here is a scale drawing of the infield at Yankee Stadium. The *scale* is the ratio that compares the measurements in the drawing or model to the actual measurements. The scale of the drawing is 1 cm = 45 ft, which means that 1 cm on the drawing represents 45 ft on the actual field.

Example: If the distance between the bases in the drawing is 2 centimeters, what is the actual distance between the bases?

$\dfrac{1 \text{ cm}}{45 \text{ ft}} = \dfrac{\text{drawing length}}{\text{actual length}}$ Write a ratio for the scale.

$\dfrac{1 \text{ cm}}{45 \text{ ft}} = \dfrac{2 \text{ cm}}{n \text{ ft}}$ Set up a proportion, letting n represent the actual length. Check that the same units are in the numerators, and the same units are in the denominators.

$1n = 45 \cdot 2$ Cross-multiply.

$n = 90$ Simplify.

A distance of 2 centimeters on the drawing represents a distance of 90 feet between the bases.

Maps are also usually drawn to scale.

Example: The distance between 2 points on a map measures 1.5 inches. Find the actual distance if the scale of the map is 1 in. = 120 mi.

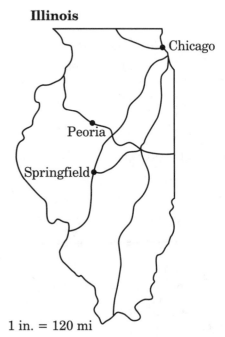

Illinois

$\dfrac{1 \text{ in.}}{120 \text{ mi}} = \dfrac{\text{drawing length}}{\text{actual length}}$ Write a ratio for the scale.

$\dfrac{1 \text{ in.}}{120 \text{ mi}} = \dfrac{1.5 \text{ in.}}{n \text{ mi}}$ Set up a proportion, letting n represent the actual distance. Check the units in the numerators and denominators.

$1n = 120 \cdot 1.5$ Cross-multiply.

$n = 180$ Simplify.

A distance of 1.5 inches on the map represents a distance of 180 miles.

Example: Adam has a radio-controlled race car model that is $\frac{1}{12}$ actual size. If the model is 14 inches long, what is the actual length of the race car?

$\frac{1}{12} = \frac{\text{model length}}{\text{actual length}}$ Write a ratio for the scale.

$\frac{1}{12} = \frac{14 \text{ in.}}{n \text{ in.}}$ Set up a proportion, letting n represent the actual length.

$1n = 12 \cdot 14$ Cross-multiply.

$n = 168$ Simplify.

To give the answer in feet, divide by 12. $168 \div 12 = 14$ feet.

The actual length is 168 inches, or 14 feet.

Example: Annette wants to make a model of her bedroom. Her bed is 75 in. long. If she uses a scale of 1:15, how long should she make the model of her bed?

$\frac{1}{15} = \frac{\text{model length}}{\text{actual length}}$ Write a ratio for the scale. Remember that the ratio 1:15 can be rewritten as the fraction $\frac{1}{15}$.

$\frac{1}{15} = \frac{n \text{ in.}}{75 \text{ in.}}$ Set up a proportion, letting n represent the model length.

$75 = 15n$ Cross-multiply.

$5 = n$ Solve.

The model of the bed should be 5 inches long.

Self-Test

Circle the letter of the correct answer.

1. The distance between two cities on a map measures 3 inches. Find the actual distance if the scale on the map is 1 in. = 120 mi.

   A. 40 in.   C. 360 in.

   B. 40 mi   D. 360 mi

2. Brent has a toy truck that is $\frac{1}{64}$ actual size. If the model is 0.25 ft long, what is the actual length of the truck?

   A. 16 ft   C. 64 ft

   B. 25 ft   D. 256 ft

Check your answer.

D is correct.

$\frac{1 \text{ in.}}{120 \text{ mi}} = \frac{\text{drawing length}}{\text{actual length}}$

$\frac{1 \text{ in.}}{120 \text{ mi}} = \frac{3 \text{ in.}}{n \text{ mi}}$

$1n = 120 \cdot 3$

$n = 360$

The actual distance is 360 mi.

A is correct.

$\frac{1}{64} = \frac{\text{model length}}{\text{actual length}}$

$\frac{1}{64} = \frac{0.25 \text{ ft}}{n \text{ ft}}$

$1n = 64 \cdot 0.25$

$n = 16$

The actual length of the truck is 16 ft.

Practice

Interpreting Scale Drawings and Models

Circle the letter of the correct answer.

1. On a scale drawing of a room, 1 cm represents 6 feet. In the scale drawing the room is 3 cm long. How long is the actual room?

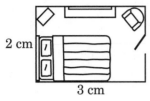

2 cm

3 cm

   A. 14 ft
   B. 16 ft
   C. 18 ft
   D. 31.5 ft

2. On a scale drawing of a swimming pool, 1 cm represents 4 feet. In the scale drawing, the swimming pool is 5.5 cm long. How long is the actual swimming pool?

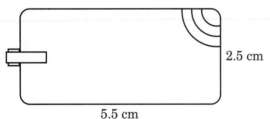

5.5 cm

2.5 cm

   A. 9.5 ft
   B. 22 ft
   C. 22.5 ft
   D. 33.75 ft

3. On a scale drawing of a tennis court, 1 cm represents 10 feet. What is the actual distance, shown on the drawing as 3.9 cm?

   A. 36 ft
   B. 39 ft
   C. 72 ft
   D. 78 ft

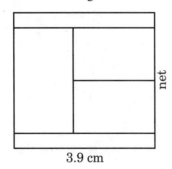

net

3.9 cm

4. On a scale drawing of a football field, 1 cm represents 20 yards. What is the width, in yards, of the football field?

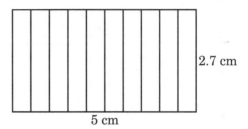

2.7 cm

5 cm

   A. 20 yd   C. 54 yd
   B. 27 yd   D. 100 yd

5. The distance between two cities on a map is 4 cm. The scale on the map says 1 cm = 35 km. What is the actual distance between the cities?

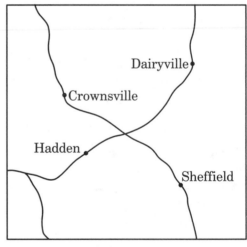

Dairyville

Crownsville

Hadden

Sheffield

1 cm = 35 mi.

   A. 35 km   C. 135 km
   B. 70 km   D. 140 km

6. The distance between two cities on a map is 5 cm. The scale on the map says 1 cm = 25 mi. What is the actual distance between the cities?

   A. 125 mi   C. 175 mi
   B. 150 mi   D. 180 mi

Lesson 38: Interpreting Scale Drawings and Models

7. The actual distance between two cities is 50 mi. The scale on the map says 1 in. = 40 mi. What is the distance between the cities on the map?

   A. 0.8 in.

   B. 1 in.

   C. 1.25 in.

   D. 1.5 in.

8. The actual distance between two cities is 252 km. The scale on the map says 1 cm = 60 km. What is the distance between the cities on the map?

   A. 4.2 cm

   B. 4.6 cm

   C. 4.8 cm

   D. 5 cm

9. An architect made a blueprint for a new house. The scale on the blueprint reads $\frac{1}{8}$ in. = 1 ft. The bedroom is to be 18 ft long. How long is this on the blueprint?

   A. $2\frac{1}{8}$ in.

   B. $2\frac{1}{4}$ in.

   C. $2\frac{1}{2}$ in.

   D. $2\frac{3}{4}$ in.

10. An architect made a blueprint for a new house. The scale on the blueprint reads $\frac{1}{4}$ in. = 1 ft. If the dining room on the blueprint is 3 inches long, how long will the actual dining room be?

   A. $3\frac{1}{4}$ ft

   B. 9 ft

   C. 12 ft

   D. 16 ft

11. Laura has a model train set. The scale of the model is $\frac{1}{87}$. A piece of track is 9 inches long. What is the actual length of the track?

   A. 723 in.

   B. 763 in.

   C. 766 in.

   D. 783 in.

12. A model car kit has a scale of $\frac{1}{24}$. If the model is 6.9 inches long, how long is the actual car?

   A. 155.6 in.

   B. 162.6 in.

   C. 165.6 in.

   D. 166.6 in.

13. A model car is $8\frac{1}{2}$ inches long. The scale is $\frac{1}{18}$. What is the actual length?

   A. 93 in.

   B. 144 in.

   C. 148 in.

   D. 153 in.

14. A decorator uses miniature furniture to plan how to arrange furniture. A miniature sofa is 3.5 inches long. If the scale of the furniture is 1 to 24, what is the actual length of the sofa?

   A. 72.5 in.

   B. 75 in.

   C. 80 in.

   D. 84 in.

15. Chris has a scale model of a car that is $\frac{1}{64}$ actual size. If the model is 6.2 cm long, what is the actual length of the car?

   A. 369.8 cm

   B. 384 cm

   C. 386.8 cm

   D. 396.8 cm

Computing Perimeter and Circumference of Geometric Figures

LESSON 39

You will learn how to compute:
• the perimeter of basic polygons
• the circumference of a circle

Key Words: perimeter, circumference, pi, diameter, radius

Xavier wants to create a garden in his back yard. He has 24 meters of fencing to enclose the garden. He must choose one of the following plans that were suggested by family members. To decide which plan to use, he must find the perimeter of each potential garden to see if he has enough fencing. The *perimeter* of a polygon is the sum of the lengths of the sides. Use P for perimeter.

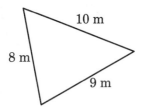

Triangular Garden
$P = 10 + 8 + 9$
$P = 27$

Square Garden
$P = 7 + 7 + 7 + 7$, or
$P = 4(7)$
$P = 28$

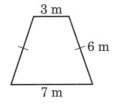

Trapezoidal Garden
The length of the side that is not labeled is equal to the length of the side with the identical mark.
$P = 7 + 6 + 3 + 6$
$P = 22$

The perimeter of the triangular garden is 27 meters. Xavier does not have enough fencing for this plan.

The perimeter of the square garden is 28 meters. Xavier does not have enough fencing for this plan.

The perimeter of the trapezoidal garden is 22 meters. Xavier should use this plan.

Example: Calculate the perimeter of a rectangle with a height of 10.2 and width of 15.3.

The opposite sides of a rectangle are equal.
$P = 10.2 + 10.2 + 15.3 + 15.3 = 51$
The perimeter is 51 units.

Example: Calculate the perimeter of the parallelogram.

The opposite sides of a parallelogram are equal.
$P = 5 + 5 + 6 + 6 = 22$
The perimeter is 22 yards.

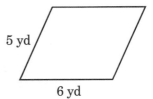

5 yd

6 yd

Xavier would also like to create a circular pond in his back yard. He plans to place a border around the pond. To find the length of the border, he will need to find the circumference of the pond.

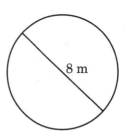

The *circumference* of a circle is the distance around the circle. The formula for finding the circumference of a circle is:

Circumference = π · diameter, or $C = \pi d$

The number *pi* (π) has an approximate value of 3.14. The *diameter* is the length of a segment that joins two points of the circle and contains the center.

$C = \pi d$ The circumference of the pond   Notice that ≈ is used instead
$C \approx 3.14(8)$ is approximately 25.12 meters.   of = when the approximation
$C \approx 25.12$ of π is used.

Xavier needs a border that is approximately 25.12 meters long.

Example: Find the circumference of the given circle.

The length shown on the diagram is called the radius. The *radius* is the length of a segment from the center of the circle to a point on the circle. The diameter is twice the radius.

$2(10.5) = 21$ $C = \pi d$
The diameter is 21 cm. $C \approx 3.14(21)$
                             $C \approx 65.94$

The circumference is approximately 65.94 cm.

Self-Test

Circle the letter of the correct answer.

Hanna needs to know the perimeter of a 4 inch by 7 inch rectangular photograph in order to have it framed. What is the perimeter of the photograph?

A. 11 inches   C. 22 inches

B. 15 inches   D. 28 inches

Check your answer.

C is correct. To find the perimeter of a rectangle, add the lengths of its four sides.

4 + 7 + 4 + 7 = 22

Practice

Computing Perimeter and Circumference of Geometric Figures

Circle the letter of the correct answer. Use 3.14 for π.

1. Find the perimeter of the parallelogram.

   A. 10 ft
   B. 14 ft
   C. 25 ft
   D. 50 ft

   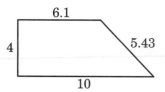

2. What is the approximate circumference of a circle whose diameter is 8 inches?

   A. 25.12 inches
   B. 32 inches
   C. 32.14 inches
   D. 50.24 inches

3. What is the perimeter of the trapezoid?

   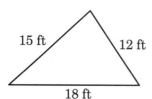

   A. 25.53 units
   B. 40 units
   C. 50.43 units
   D. 61 units

4. Ji created a triangular mural for a community center.

   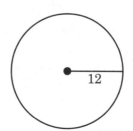

   What is the perimeter of the mural?

   A. 45 feet
   B. 80 feet
   C. 216 feet
   D. 270 feet

5. Jonah is building a square play area for his dog. If the length of one side of the play area is 10 feet, how many feet of fencing material will he need?

   A. 20 feet
   B. 40 feet
   C. 80 feet
   D. 100 feet

6. Find the approximate circumference of the circle.

   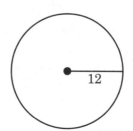

   A. 36 units
   B. 37.68 units
   C. 63.14 units
   D. 75.36 units

7. The length of one side of a triangle is 2.38 units. All three sides of the triangle have the same length. What is the perimeter of the triangle?

   A. 2.38 units
   B. 4.76 units
   C. 7.14 units
   D. 9.52 units

8. What is the perimeter of the rectangle?

   A. 32.4 m
   B. 64.8 m
   C. 87.8 m
   D. 110.8 m

9. The width and length of 4 rectangles are given below. Which rectangle has a perimeter of 36 inches?

   A. $w = 21$ inches; $l = 15$ inches
   B. $w = 44$ inches; $l = 8$ inches
   C. $w = 6$ inches; $l = 6$ inches
   D. $w = 8$ inches; $l = 10$ inches

10. The length of one side of a square tile is 20.25 cm. What is the perimeter of the tile?

   A. 40.5 cm
   B. 81 cm
   C. 220.25 cm
   D. 400 cm

11. What is the approximate circumference of the circle?

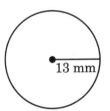

13 mm

   A. 26 mm
   B. 40.82 mm
   C. 81.64 mm
   D. 122 mm

12. Which figure has the greatest perimeter?

   A. a square with a side length of 10
   B. a rectangle with a length of 12 and width of 9
   C. a triangle with sides lengths of 8, 14, and 19
   D. a trapezoid with side lengths of 5, 5, 12, and 14

13. Lars is putting a wallpaper border around a 9 ft by 12 ft rectangular room. What is the perimeter of the room?

   A. 21 ft
   B. 42 ft
   C. 108 ft
   D. 144 ft

14. Which figure has the greatest circumference?

   A. a circle with a radius of 6
   B. a circle with a diameter of 12.5
   C. a circle with a diameter of 14
   D. a circle with a radius of 5.4

15. Find the perimeter of the trapezoid.

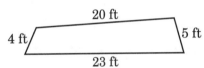

   A. 52 feet
   B. 80 feet
   C. 100 feet
   D. 115 feet

16. Which figure has a perimeter of 30 units?

   A. a triangle with a side lengths of 6, 3, and 2
   B. a rectangle with a length of 20 and width of 10
   C. a trapezoid with sides lengths of 12, 8, 6, and 4
   D. a square with a side length of 30.

Computing Area of Geometric Figures

LESSON 40

You will learn how to find:
• the area of basic polygons
• the area of a circle

Greta and Julio own a home remodeling business. A customer has sent them a drawing of two rooms in his home that need new carpet. To determine the cost of carpeting these two rooms, Greta and Julio must find the area of each room.

Area is a measure of the size of a flat surface. The units for area are square units such as square feet, or ft².

To find the area of a rectangle, use the formula:

Area of a rectangle = length · width, or $A = lw$

Example: Find the area of Room A.

Area of a rectangle = length · width, or $A = lw$

Area = 12 feet · 9 feet = 108 ft²

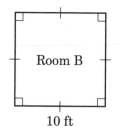

Room A   9 ft
12 ft

Example: Find the area of Room B.

Room B is a square. A square is a type of rectangle, so the same formula applies.

Area of a square = length · width, or

Area of a square = side · side, or $A = s^2$

Area = (10 ft)² = 100 ft²

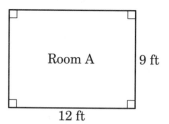

Room B
10 ft

To find the area of a parallelogram, multiply the base and the height. Any side can be the base. The height is the distance from the base to the opposite side; it is perpendicular to the base.

Example: Find the area of the parallelogram.

Area of a parallelogram = base · height, or $A = bh$

Area = 6 cm · 4 cm = 24 cm²

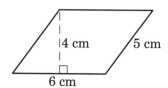

4 cm   5 cm
6 cm

The area of the triangle in the figure below is half the area of the rectangle. The length and width of the rectangle are the base and height of the triangle. To find the area of the triangle, use the formula $A = \frac{1}{2}bh$.

Example: What is the area of the shaded region?

Area of a triangle = $\frac{1}{2}$ · base · height, or $A = \frac{1}{2}bh$

Area = $\frac{1}{2}$ · 4 inches · 3.6 inches = 7.2 square inches

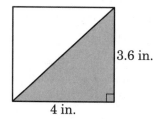

3.6 in.
4 in.

To find the area of a trapezoid, you must be able to identify the two bases and the height. The bases are the parallel sides. The height is the distance between the bases and is perpendicular to the bases. To find the area of a trapezoid, use the formula $A = \frac{1}{2}h(b_1 + b_2)$, where h is the height and b_1 and b_2 are the bases.

Example: Find the area of the trapezoid.

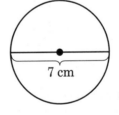

Area of a trapezoid $= \frac{1}{2} \cdot$ height $\cdot$ (base 1 + base 2), or
$A = \frac{1}{2}h(b_1 + b_2)$
Area $= \frac{1}{2} \cdot 10$ m $\cdot$ (14 m + 16 m)
Area $= \frac{1}{2} \cdot 10$ m $\cdot$ 30 m = 150 m^2

The formula for finding the area of a circle is given below.

Area $= \pi \cdot$ radius^2, or $A = \pi r^2$

The approximate value of the number π (pi) is 3.14.

Example: Find the area of a circle whose radius is 3 units long.

Area in terms of π	**Approximate area, using $\pi \approx 3.14$**
$A = \pi r^2$	$A = \pi r^2$
$A = \pi(3 \text{ units})^2$	$A \approx 3.14 \cdot (3 \text{ units})^2$
$A = 9\pi \text{ units}^2$	$A \approx 3.14 \cdot 9 \text{ units}^2$
	$A \approx 28.26 \text{ units}^2$

Example: Find the approximate area of the circle.

Find the length of the radius. $\qquad A = \pi r^2$
radius = diameter $\div$ 2 $\qquad A \approx 3.14 \cdot (3.5 \text{ cm})^2$
radius = 7 cm $\div$ 2 = 3.5 cm $\qquad A \approx 3.14 \cdot 12.25 \text{ cm}^2$
$\qquad\qquad\qquad\qquad\qquad\qquad A \approx 38.465 \text{ cm}^2$

Self-Test

Circle the letter of the correct answer.

What is the area of the trapezoid?

A. 28 square feet C. 96 square feet

B. 29 square feet D. 112 square feet

Check your answer.

C is correct.

$A = \frac{1}{2}h(b_1 + b_2) = \frac{1}{2} \cdot 8 \cdot (10 + 14) = 96$

Practice

Computing Area of Geometric Figures

Circle the letter of the correct answer. Use 3.14 for π.

1. Find the area of the parallelogram.

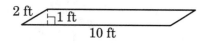

2 ft ⌐1 ft
10 ft

   A.   5 ft²

   B. 10 ft²

   C. 20 ft²

   D. 24 ft²

2. Which rectangle has an area of 16 m²?

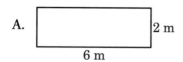

   A.   2 m
            6 m

   B.   2 m
          16 m

                2 m
   C.   8 m

                2 m
   D.   4 m

3. What is the approximate area of a circle whose radius is 4 inches?

   A.   3.14 inches²

   B. 12.56 inches²

   C. 25.12 inches²

   D. 50.24 inches²

4. What is the area of the trapezoid?

   A. 12 square units

   B. 20 square units

   C. 60 square units

   D. 75 square units

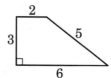

2
3   5
6

5. What is the area of the figure?

   A. 30 feet²

   B. 32.5 feet²

   C. 60 feet²

   D. 78 feet²

12 ft 13 ft
5 ft

6. Randi will carpet a square room. The length of one side of the room is 11 feet. How much carpeting will she need?

   A.   22 feet²

   B.   44 feet²

   C.   88 feet²

   D. 121 feet²

7. Find the approximate area of the circle.

   A.   15.7 square units

   B.   31.4 square units

   C.   78.5 square units

   D. 314 square units

5

8. The length of the base of a triangle is 3 cm and the height is 2 cm. What is the area of the triangle?

   A.   2 square cm

   B.   3 square cm

   C.   6 square cm

   D. 12 square cm

9. Which circle has an area of approximately 12.56 mm²?

 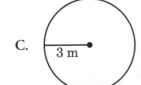

A.   C.

B. 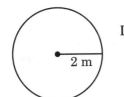 D.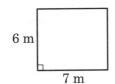

10. What is the area of the rectangle?

A. 13 m²
B. 21 m²
C. 26 m²
D. 42 m²

6 m 7 m

11. The base and height of 4 parallelograms are given below. Which parallelogram has an area of 48 inches²?

A. $b = 10$ inches; $h = 14$ inches
B. $b = 4$ inches; $h = 8$ inches
C. $b = 8$ inches; $h = 6$ inches
D. $b = 6$ inches; $h = 16$ inches

12. The length of one side of a square is 2.5. What is the area of the square?

A. 6.25 square units
B. 62.5 square units
C. 625 square units
D. 6,250 square units

13. What is the approximate area of the circle?

A. 18.84 yd²
B. 113.04 yd²
C. 226.08 yd²
D. 452.16 yd²

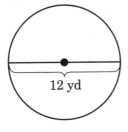

12 yd

14. Which figure will have the greatest area?

A. a square with a side length of 2
B. a rectangle with a length of 2 and width of 1
C. a triangle with a base of 2 and a height of 2
D. a circle with a radius of 2

15. What is the area of a rectangle whose length is 9 ft and width is 2.5 ft?

A. 6.5 ft²
B. 11.5 ft²
C. 22.5 ft²
D. 23 ft²

16. Which figure will have the greatest area?

A. a circle with a radius of 2
B. a circle with a diameter of 6.09
C. a circle with a diameter of 7
D. a circle with a radius of 4.26

17. Find the area of the trapezoid.

A. 20.7 feet²
B. 28.6 feet²
C. 41.4 feet²
D. 54.2 feet²

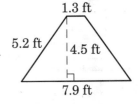

1.3 ft
5.2 ft 4.5 ft
7.9 ft

18. Which figure will have an area of 3.14 square units?

A. a square with a side length of 4.25
B. a rectangle with a length of 3 and width of 2.75
C. a triangle with a base of 3 and a height of 2.75
D. a circle with a radius of 1

Graphing Simple Figures and Computing Length and Area

LESSON 41

You will learn how to:

- graph simple figures on a coordinate plane
- compute lengths and areas on a coordinate plane
- estimate lengths and areas on a coordinate plane

Example: Graph the figure whose vertices are $A(1, 1)$, $B(1, 3)$, $C(4, 3)$, and $D(4, 1)$.

What kind of polygon is $ABCD$?

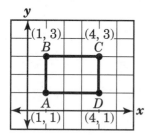

$ABCD$ is a rectangle.

Find the lengths of $\overline{AB}$ and $\overline{AD}$.

Count the spaces between A and B.

$AB = 2$ units

Count the spaces between A and D.

$AD = 3$ units

Find the perimeter.

Add the lengths of all the sides.

$P = 2 + 3 + 2 + 3$
$\quad = 10$.

The perimeter is 10 units.

Find the area.

Count the square units inside, or use the formula:

$A = bh$
$\quad = (2)(3)$
$\quad = 6$

The area is 6 square units.

Example: Graph the figure whose vertices are $P(2, 1)$, $Q(2, 7)$, and $R(6, 1)$.

What kind of polygon is PQR?

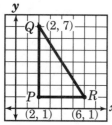

PQR is a triangle.

Find the lengths of $\overline{PQ}$ and $\overline{PR}$.

Count the spaces between each pair of points on the coordinate plane.

$PQ = 6$ units

$PR = 4$ units

Find the area.

The base and height of this triangle are $\overline{PR}$ and $\overline{PQ}$.

$A = \frac{1}{2}bh$
$\quad = \frac{1}{2}(4)(6) = 12$

The area is 12 square units.

Example: Graph the figure whose vertices are $K(-1, 3)$, $L(2, 3)$, $M(6, 1)$, and $N(-3, 1)$.

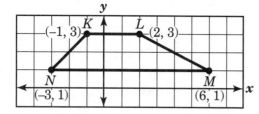

What kind of polygon is $KLMN$?

$KLMN$ is a trapezoid.

Find the area.

The bases are $KL = 3$ and $NM = 9$. The height is 2.

$A = \frac{1}{2}(b_1 + b_2)h$
$\quad = \frac{1}{2}(3 + 9)2 = 12$

The area is 12 square units.

Example: Graph the figure whose vertices are $R(-1, -1)$, $S(3, -1)$, $T(7, 2)$, and $U(3, 2)$.

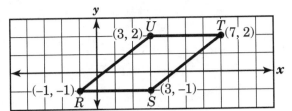

What kind of polygon is *RSTU*? *RSTU* is a parallelogram.

Find the area.

You can use $\overline{RS}$ as the base; then the height is 3.

$A = (b)(h)$

$\quad = (4)(3) = 12$

The area is 12 square units.

Example: What is a good estimate for the area of this circle?

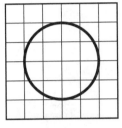

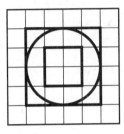

You can estimate the area by drawing squares. Draw one square outside and one square inside.

The area of the outside square is 16 square units.

The area of the inside square is 4 square units.

The area of the circle is between 4 square units and 16 square units, but closer to 16, so 12 would be a good estimate.

Self-Test

Circle the letter of the correct answer.

The vertices of a polygon are (1, 2), (1, 8), and (4, 4). What is the area of the polygon?

A. 7 square units

B. 8 square units

C. 9 square units

D. 10 square units

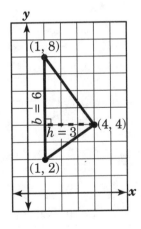

Check your answer.

C is correct.

$A = \frac{1}{2}bh = \frac{1}{2}(6)(3) = 9$

Practice

Graphing Simple Figures and Computing Length and Area

Circle the letter of the correct answer.

1. The vertices of a polygon are located at (1, 1), (4, 1), and (4, 4). What is the area of the polygon?

   A. 4.5 square units

   B. 7 square units

   C. 8.5 square units

   D. 9 square units

2. Which is the best estimate for the area of the figure?

   A. 15 square units

   B. 17 square units

   C. 20 square units

   D. 22 square units

3. The vertices of a polygon are located at (−2, −1), (−2, −4), (4, −4), and (4, −1). What is the area of the polygon?

   A. 6 square units

   B. 9 square units

   C. 12 square units

   D. 18 square units

4. Which is the best estimate for the area of the figure?

   A. 10 square units

   B. 12 square units

   C. 14 square units

   D. 16 square units

5. The vertices of a polygon are located at (4, −2), (0, −2), (4, 3), and (0, 3). What is the perimeter of the polygon?

   A. 9 units

   B. 15 units

   C. 18 units

   D. 20 units

6. The vertices of a polygon are located at (2, 3), (10, 3), and (10, 8). What is the area of the polygon?

   A. 20 square units

   B. 25 square units

   C. 40 square units

   D. 64 square units

7. Which is the name for the shape formed by the points (1, 3), (2, 3), (2, 4), and (1, 7)?

   A. square

   B. parallelogram

   C. trapezoid

   D. rectangle

8. The vertices of a polygon are located at (1, 1), (1, 3), (−1, 3), and (−1, 1). What is the area of the polygon?

   A. 2 square units

   B. 4 square units

   C. 6 square units

   D. 8 square units

9. What is the length of one side of the square formed by the points (−3, 2), (−6, 2), (−6, 5), and (−3, 5)?

   A. 1 unit

   B. 2 units

   C. 3 units

   D. 4 units

10. Find the area of the polygon with vertices (−4, 3), (1, 3), (−5, 0), and (0, 0).

    A. 12 square units

    B. 15 square units

    C. 16 square units

    D. 20 square units

11. The vertices of a polygon are located at $(-2, 0)$, $(-3, 0)$, $(-3, 5)$, and $(-2, 5)$. What is the area of the polygon?

    A.   5 square units

    B.   6 square units

    C. 20 square units

    D. 25 square units

12. Which is the name for the shape formed by the points $(-5, -2)$, $(-6, -4)$, $(-2, -4)$, and $(-2, -2)$?

    A. square

    B. parallelogram

    C. trapezoid

    D. rectangle

13. Which is the name for the shape formed by the points $(0, 3)$, $(3, 3)$, $(1, 0)$, and $(-2, 0)$?

    A. square

    B. parallelogram

    C. trapezoid

    D. rectangle

14. The vertices of a polygon are located at $(2, -1)$, $(6, -1)$, $(5, -4)$, and $(1, -4)$. What is the area of the polygon?

    A.   4 square units

    B. 12 square units

    C. 14 square units

    D. 16 square units

15. What is the perimeter of the rectangle formed by the points $(-5, 0)$, $(-2, 0)$, $(-2, 2)$, and $(-5, 2)$?

    A.   5 units

    B.   6 units

    C.   9 units

    D. 10 units

16. What is the area of the figure formed by the points $(1, 2)$, $(4, 1)$, $(4, 8)$, and $(1, 6)$?

    A. $\frac{33}{2}$ square units

    B. 21 square units

    C. 33 square units

    D. $\frac{77}{2}$ square units

17. The vertices of a polygon are located at $(3, 0)$, $(-3, 0)$, $(-3, 5)$, and $(3, 5)$. What is the perimeter of the polygon?

    A. 11 units

    B. 20 units

    C. 22 units

    D. 30 units

18. The vertices of a polygon are located at $(-2, 2)$, $(-4, -2)$, $(5, -2)$, and $(2, 2)$. What is the area of the polygon?

    A. 16 square units

    B. 17 square units

    C. 26 square units

    D. 52 square units

19. Which is the name for the shape formed by the points $(0, 0)$, $(3, 0)$, $(3, 2)$, and $(0, 2)$?

    A. square

    B. triangle

    C. trapezoid

    D. rectangle

20. The vertices of a polygon are located at $(-2, 2)$, $(0, 6)$, and $(2, 2)$. What is the area of the polygon?

    A.   6 square units

    B.   8 square units

    C. 10 square units

    D. 12 square units

Graphing Translations and Reflections on a Coordinate Plane

LESSON 42

You will learn how to graph:
- the image of a figure under translation
- the image of a figure under a reflection

Key Words: transformation, image, preimage, translation, reflection

Transformations are movements of geometric figures on a coordinate plane. The figure that results from a transformation is called the *image*, and the original figure is called the *preimage*. A capital letter is used to name any vertex in the preimage. The corresponding point in the image is named by the same capital letter, along with the symbol ′, read "prime."

A translation is a type of transformation. You can think of a *translation* as a slide. A figure can be translated horizontally, vertically, or both.

ABCD has been translated 5 units left, resulting in image *A′B′C′D′*. Notice that the x-coordinate of each image point is 5 less than the x-coordinate of the corresponding preimage point. For example, *C* has coordinates (9, 5) and *C′* has coordinates (4, 5).

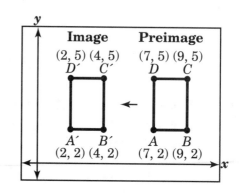

Example: Translate figure *WXY* 3 units right and 2 units up.

You can locate the image of an entire polygon by locating the images of its vertices. Count 3 units right and 2 units up from each vertex in the preimage. If you need the coordinates of a point in the image, add 3 to the x-coordinate and 2 to the y-coordinate of the corresponding point in the preimage. The coordinates of *W* and *W′* are shown.

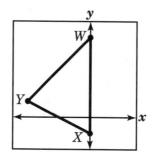

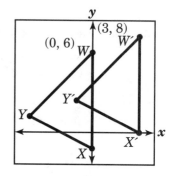

Example: The coordinates of △*PQR* are *P* (3, 1), *Q* (−1, 1), and *R* (1, 3). If △*PQR* is translated 4 units down, what are the coordinates of the image △*P′Q′R′*?

To translate 4 units down, subtract 4 from the y-coordinate of each vertex.

The coordinates of the image △*P′Q′R′* are *P′*(3, −3), *Q′*(−1, −3), and *R′*(1, −1).

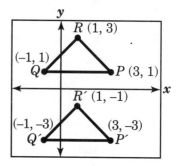

A transformation that appears to result in a mirror image is called a *reflection*. A figure can be reflected over any line.

Examples:

Reflect △*LMN* over the *y*-axis.

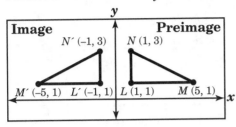

The *x*-coordinate of each image point is the opposite of the *x*-coordinate of its corresponding preimage point. The *y*-coordinates are the same.

Reflect *ABCD* over the *x*-axis.

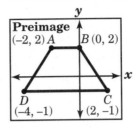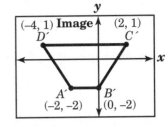

The *y*-coordinate of each image point is the opposite of the *y*-coordinate of its corresponding preimage point. The *x*-coordinates are the same.

Example: If △*ABC* is reflected over the line *x* = 4, what are the coordinates of the image △*A'B'C'*?

The distance from each image point to the line of reflection is equal to the distance from the corresponding preimage point to the line of reflection. Points *A* and *A'* are illustrated. The coordinates of the reflected image are *A'* (6, 1), *B'* (5, 2), and *C'* (7, 3).

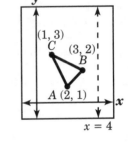

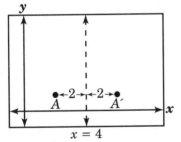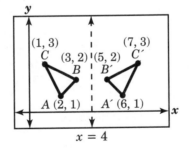

Self-Test

Circle the letter of the correct answer.

Identify the transformation.

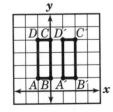

A. *ABCD* is translated 2 units right.
B. *ABCD* is reflected over the y-axis.
C. *ABCD* is translated 1 unit right.
D. *ABCD* is reflected over the x-axis.

Check your answer.

A is correct.

Each point in the image is exactly two units to the right of its corresponding point of the preimage.

Practice

Graphing Translations and Reflections on a Coordinate Plane

Circle the letter of the correct answer.

1. Identify the transformation.

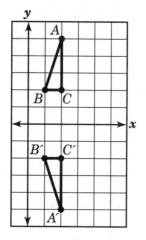

A. △ABC is translated 4 units down.
B. △ABC is reflected over the y-axis.
C. △ABC is translated 4 units up.
D. △ABC is reflected over the x-axis.

2. Which of the following figures E'F'G' is the image of figure EFG that results from translating figure EFG 3 units up?

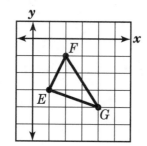

A. 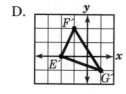 C.

B. D.

3. Which of the following figures A'B'C'D' is the image of figure ABCD that results from reflecting figure ABCD over the x-axis?

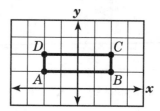

A. 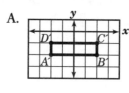 C.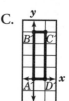

B. 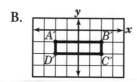 D.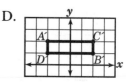

4. Identify the transformation.

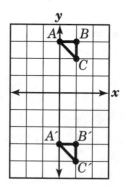

A. △ABC is translated 6 units up.
B. △ABC is reflected over the y-axis.
C. △ABC is translated 6 units down.
D. △ABC is reflected over the x-axis.

Lesson 42: Graphing Translations and Reflections on a Coordinate Plane

5. Reflect figure *ABCD* over the *y*-axis.

A.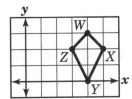

C.

B.

D.

6. Translate figure *WXYZ* 5 units left.

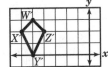

A.

C.

B.

D.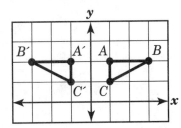

7. Identify the transformation.

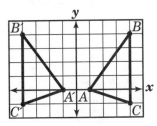

A. △*ABC* is translated 8 units left.

B. △*ABC* is reflected over the *y*-axis.

C. △*ABC* is translated 2 units left.

D. △*ABC* is reflected over the *x*-axis.

8. The coordinates of △*STU* are *S* (0, 4), *T* (0, 0), and *U* (2, 0). The figure is reflected over the *x*-axis to form △*S'T'U'*. What are the coordinates of *S'*?

A. (0, 4)

B. (0, −4)

C. (−2, 0)

D. (0, 0)

9. The coordinates of △*PQR* are *P* (−3, −1), *Q* (−2, 2), and *R* (−1, −2). The figure is translated 6 units up to form △*P'Q'R'*. What are the coordinates of *P'*?

A. (3, −1)

B. (−3, 5)

C. (−2, 8)

D. (−3, 6)

10. Identify the transformation.

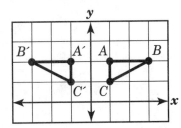

A. △*ABC* is translated 2 units left.

B. △*ABC* is reflected over the *y*-axis.

C. △*ABC* is translated 6 units left.

D. △*ABC* is reflected over the *x*-axis.

11. The coordinates of figure *DEFG* are *D* (−1, 3), *E* (−4, 3), *F* (−4, −1), and *G* (−1, −1). The figure is translated 9 units to the right to form figure *D'E'F'G'*. What are the coordinates of *E'*?

A. (13, 3)

B. (−4, 12)

C. (8, 3)

D. (5, 3)

Lesson 42: Graphing Translations and Reflections on a Coordinate Plane

169

Estimating and Computing Area of Irregular Figures

LESSON 43

> You will learn how to:
> • compute and estimate the area of irregular figures

Paul is creating a mural for his school's cafeteria. Here is his diagram for the mural.

Paul needs to know the area of the mural to determine how much paint to buy. How can Paul determine the area of the figure?

You have learned formulas you can use to determine the area of figures such as parallelograms and circles. There is no simple formula for the area of this specific figure. But, you can separate an irregular figure into simpler figures to find the area.

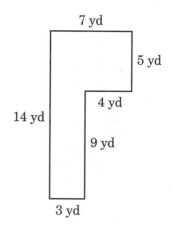

Example: What will be the area of Paul's mural?

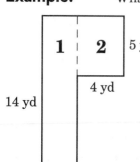

Separate the figure into two rectangles, find the area of each rectangle, and add the areas to get the area of the figure.

$A = lw = 14 \cdot 3 = 42 \text{ yd}^2$ Find the area of the first rectangle.

$A = lw = 5 \cdot 4 = 20 \text{ yd}^2$ Find the area of the second rectangle.

$42 \text{ yd}^2 + 20 \text{ yd}^2 = 62 \text{ yd}^2$ Add the two areas.

Example: What is the area of the figure?

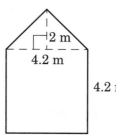

Separate the figure into a triangle and a square. The triangle has a height of 2 m and the length of the base is 4.2 m. The length of a side of the square is 4.2 m.

$A = \frac{1}{2} bh = \frac{1}{2} \cdot 4.2 \cdot 2 = 4.2 \text{ m}^2$ Find the area of the triangle.

$A = s^2 = 4.2^2 = 17.64 \text{ m}^2$ Find the area of the square.

$4.2 \text{ m}^2 + 17.64 \text{ m}^2 = 21.84 \text{ m}^2$ Add the two areas.

Many irregular figures are formed by removing one simple figure from another. To find the area of such figures, subtract the area of the section that is not included in the figure from the total area.

Example: Paul created a circle to hang near the mural. He cut a circle with a radius of 2 inches from a square piece of paper. The length of one side of the square was 4 inches. Find the area of the paper that remained after Paul cut out the circle.

The shaded region represents the remaining paper.

$A = s^2 = 4^2 = 16$ sq in.	Find the area of the square.
$A = \pi r^2 \approx 3.14 \cdot 2^2 = 12.56$ sq in.	Find the area of the circle.
16 sq in. $-$ 12.56 sq in. $=$ 3.44 sq in.	Subtract the areas.

The approximate area of the remaining paper is 3.44 sq in.

Example: Find the approximate area of the shaded region.

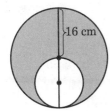

The radius of the larger circle is 16 cm. The diameter of the smaller circle equals the radius of the larger circle, so the radius of the smaller circle is 8 cm.

$A = \pi r^2 \approx 3.14 \cdot 16^2 = 803.84$ cm^2	Find the area of the larger circle.
$A = \pi r^2 \approx 3.14 \cdot 8^2 = 200.96$ cm^2	Find the area of the smaller circle.
803.84 cm^2 $-$ 200.96 cm^2 $=$ 602.88 cm^2	Subtract the areas.

The area of the shaded region is approximately 602.88 cm^2.

Example: Estimate the area of the figure.

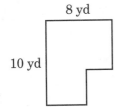

The figure is an 8 by 10 rectangle with a cutout less than $\frac{1}{4}$ of its area.

$A = lw = 10 \cdot 8 = 80$	The area of the 8 by 10 rectangle is 80 yd^2.
$\frac{1}{4}(80) = 20$	The area of the cutout is less than 20 yd^2.
$80 - 20 = 60$	The area of the figure is more than 60 yd^2.

Area of the figure is between 60 yd^2 and 80 yd^2.

Self-Test

Circle the letter of the correct answer.

What is the approximate area of the figure?

A. 33.87 in.^{2}
B. 48 in.^{2}
C. 62.13 in.^{2}
D. 76.26 in.^{2}

Check your answer.

C is correct.
area of rectangle = 6 in. $\cdot$ 8 in. = 48 in.^{2}
area of half circle $\approx \frac{1}{2} \cdot 3.14 \cdot 3^2$ = 14.13 in.^{2}
area of figure $\approx$ 48 in.^{2} + 14.13 in.^{2} = 62.13 in.^{2}

Practice

Estimating and Computing Area of Irregular Figures

Circle the letter of the correct answer. Use 3.14 for pi.

1. Estimate the area of the figure.

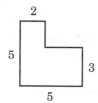

    A.   6 square units

    B.   12.5 square units

    C.   18 square units

    D.   25 square units

2. Find the area of the shaded region.

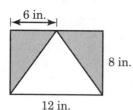

    A.   6 in.^{2}

    B.   36 in.^{2}

    C.   40 in.^{2}

    D.   48 in.^{2}

3. Find the approximate area of the shaded region.

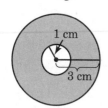

    A.   3.14 cm^2

    B.   25.12 cm^2

    C.   28.26 cm^2

    D.   31.4 cm^2

4. A 5 inch by 3 inch rectangle is removed from a 10 inch square piece of paper. What is the area of the remaining paper?

    A.   5 in.^{2}

    B.   85 in.^{2}

    C.   115 in.^{2}

    D.   150 in.^{2}

5. What is the area of the figure in square feet?

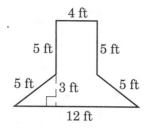

    A.   20 ft^2

    B.   24 ft^2

    C.   39 ft^2

    D.   44 ft^2

6. Find the area of the shaded region.

    A.   16 square units

    B.   18 square units

    C.   20 square units

    D.   24 square units

7. What is the area of the figure in square meters?

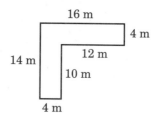

    A.   56 m^2

    B.   64 m^2

    C.   104 m^2

    D.   120 m^2

8. Irene painted one-fourth of a circle. The radius of the circle was 6 inches. What was the approximate area of the region Irene painted?

    A.   28.26 in.^{2}

    B.   56.52 in.^{2}

    C.   84.78 in.^{2}

    D.   113.04 in.^{2}

9. What is the approximate area of the figure?

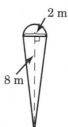

    A.   9.57 square meters

    B.   11.14 square meters

    C.   14.28 square meters

    D.   16 square meters

10. Find the area of the shaded region.

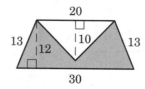

    A.   100 square units

    B.   200 square units

    C.   300 square units

    D.   400 square units

11. Find the approximate area of the shaded region.

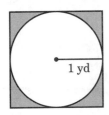

A. 0.86 yd²

B. 3 yd²

C. 3.14 yd²

D. 4 yd²

1 yd

12. Find the area of the shaded region.

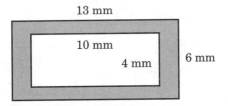

13 mm

10 mm

4 mm

6 mm

A. 38 square millimeters

B. 40 square millimeters

C. 78 square millimeters

D. 118 square millimeters

13. What is the area of the figure?

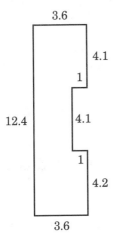

3.6

4.1

1

4.1

1

12.4

4.2

3.6

A. 40.54 square units

B. 61.76 square units

C. 75.24 square units

D. 81.08 square units

14. An 8 by 3 rectangle is removed from a circle with a radius of 20. What is the approximate area of the remaining region?

A. 38.8 square units

B. 578.5 square units

C. 870 square units

D. 1,232 square units

15. Find the approximate area of the shaded region.

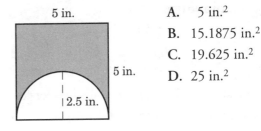

5 in.

5 in.

2.5 in.

A. 5 in.²

B. 15.1875 in.²

C. 19.625 in.²

D. 25 in.²

16. Find the area of the shaded region in square units.

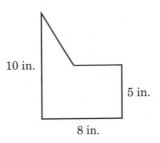

7.5

3

4.5

2

6

A. 6

B. 7.5

C. 8.5

D. 13.5

17. Which is the best estimate for the area of the figure?

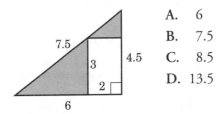

10 in.

5 in.

8 in.

A. 28 in.²

B. 40 in.²

C. 48 in.²

D. 80 in.²

18. Estimate the area of the figure.

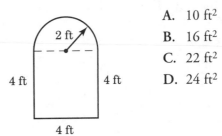

2 ft

4 ft

4 ft

4 ft

A. 10 ft²

B. 16 ft²

C. 22 ft²

D. 24 ft²

Computing Surface Area of Geometric Figures

L E S S O N   4 4

> You will learn how to:
> • use formulas for finding the surface areas of rectangular prisms and cylinders

Key Words: rectangular prism, surface area, net, congruent, cube, cylinder, lateral area

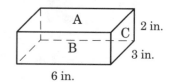

Cara wants to buy sticky-backed paper to cover a box. The box is a *rectangular prism,* or a solid with six rectangular faces. In order to know how much paper to buy, she needs to find the area of the outside surface of the box. The total area of the outside surface of a three-dimensional figure is called the *surface area.* She decides to cut apart a model of the box and lay it open. This flat pattern is called a *net.*

Example: Find the surface area of Cara's box.

The box is 6 inches long, 3 inches wide, and 2 inches high. You can see from the net that the box has 3 pairs of congruent faces. *Congruent* figures have the same shape and same size, and also have the same area. The area of each face A is 18 square inches. The area of each face B is 12 square inches. The area of each face C is 6 square inches.

To find the surface area (*SA*), multiply the area of each rectangular face by 2, and then find the sum of the areas.

$SA = 2(\text{area of A}) + 2(\text{area of B}) + 2(\text{area of C})$ or $SA = 2lw + 2lh + 2wh$
$\quad = 2 \cdot 18 + 2 \cdot 12 + 2 \cdot 6$
$\quad = 36 + 24 + 12$
$\quad = 72$

The surface area of Cara's box is 72 square inches, so she needs to buy at least that much paper to cover the box.

A *cube* is a rectangular prism with six congruent, square faces. The area of each face is s^2, where s is the length of the edge. The surface area is given by the formula $SA = 6s^2$.

Example: Find the surface area of the cube whose edge is 8 centimeters.

$SA = 6s^2$
$SA = 6 \cdot 8^2$
$SA = 384$

The surface area of the cube is 384 cm².

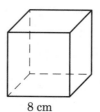

8 cm

A *cylinder* has a curved surface and two congruent parallel bases that are circles. The area of the curved surface of a cylinder is called the *lateral area*. If the curved surface is "unrolled" and laid flat, it forms a rectangle whose length is the circumference of the circular base and width is the height of the cylinder.

Recall the formulas for circles: circumference $C = 2\pi r$ area $A = \pi r^2$

    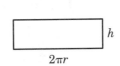   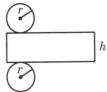

Lateral area = (length)(width)   Surface area = $LA + 2$(base area)
$$LA = 2\pi rh$$ $$SA = 2\pi rh + 2\pi r^2$$

Example: The radius of a cylinder is 4 cm and the height is 6 cm. Find the lateral area and the surface area of the cylinder.

Answers in terms of π		Answers as decimal approximations	
$LA = 2\pi rh$	$SA = 2\pi rh + 2\pi r^2$	$LA = 2\pi rh$	$SA = 2\pi rh + 2\pi r^2$
$LA = 2\pi(4)(6)$	$SA = 2\pi(4)(6) + 2\pi(4)^2$	$LA \approx 2(3.14)(4)(6)$	$SA \approx 2(3.14)(4)(6) + 2(3.14)(4)^2$
$LA = 48\pi$	$SA = 48\pi + 32\pi$	$LA \approx 150.72$	$SA \approx 150.72 + 100.48$
	$SA = 80\pi$		$SA \approx 251.2$

The lateral area is 48π cm^2, or approximately 150.72 cm^2.
The surface area is 80π cm^2, or approximately 251.2 cm^2.

Self-Test

Circle the letter of the correct answer.

1. What is the surface area of a rectangular prism with a length of 8 ft, a width of 5 ft, and a height of 3 ft?
   ($SA = 2lw + 2lh + 2wh$)

   A. 32 ft^2 C. 120 ft^2

   B. 79 ft^2 D. 158 ft^2

2. Find the surface area of a cylinder with a diameter of 10 in. and a height of 7 in.
   ($SA = 2\pi rh + 2\pi r^2$)

   A. 60π in.^{2} C. 170π in.^{2}

   B. 120π in.^{2} D. 340π in.^{2}

Check your answer.

D is correct.

$SA = 2lw + 2lh + 2wh$
$SA = 2 \cdot 8 \cdot 5 + 2 \cdot 8 \cdot 3 + 2 \cdot 5 \cdot 3$
$\quad = 80 + 48 + 30$
$\quad = 158$

B is correct.

Because the diameter is 10 in., the radius is 5 in.
$SA = 2\pi rh + 2\pi r^2$
$SA = 2\pi \cdot 5 \cdot 7 + 2\pi \cdot 5^2$
$\quad = 70\pi + 50\pi$
$\quad = 120\pi$

Practice

Computing Surface Area of Geometric Figures

Circle the letter of the correct answer.

1. What is the surface area of a rectangular prism with a length of 12 feet, a width of 7 feet, and a height of 2 feet?
   $(SA = 2lw + 2lh + 2wh)$

   A. 76 ft²
   B. 122 ft²
   C. 168 ft²
   D. 244 ft²

2. What is the surface area of a rectangular prism with a length of 6 meters, a width of 6 meters, and a height of 4 meters?
   $(SA = 2lw + 2lh + 2wh)$

   A. 32 m²
   B. 144 m²
   C. 168 m²
   D. 288 m²

3. What is the surface area of the rectangular prism shown below?
   $(SA = 2lw + 2lh + 2wh)$

   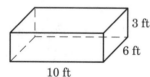

   A. 38 ft²
   B. 108 ft²
   C. 180 ft²
   D. 216 ft²

4. What is the surface area of the rectangular prism shown below?
   $(SA = 2lw + 2lh + 2wh)$

   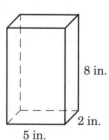

   A. 132 in.²
   B. 160 in.²
   C. 264 in.²
   D. 320 in.²

5. Miguel has a box that is 22 inches long, 16 inches wide, and 6 inches high. He wants to wrap the box with wrapping paper. What is the area of the wrapping paper that will cover the box? $(SA = 2lw + 2lh + 2wh)$

   A. 580 in.²
   B. 1,150 in.²
   C. 1,160 in.²
   D. 2,112 in.²

6. A cube has which of the following?

   A. 6 faces and 8 edges
   B. 6 faces and 12 edges
   C. 12 faces and 6 edges
   D. 8 faces and 12 edges

7. The edge of a cube is 1 centimeter long. What is the surface area of the cube?
   $(SA = 6s^2)$

   A. 1 cm²
   B. 6 cm²
   C. 12 cm²
   D. 36 cm²

8. A cube has an edge that is 5 inches long. What is the surface area of the cube?
   $(SA = 6s^2)$

   A. 30 in.²
   B. 125 in.²
   C. 150 in.²
   D. 180 in.²

9. What is the surface area of the cube shown below? ($SA = 6s^2$)

10 mm

   A.   100 mm^2

   B.   600 mm^2

   C. 1,000 mm^2

   D. 3,600 mm^2

10. Jake is painting all the faces of a large cube that will be used as a prop for a school play. The cube has an edge that measures 3 feet. What is the area that Jake needs to paint? ($SA = 6s^2$)

   A.   27 ft^2

   B.   54 ft^2

   C.   72 ft^2

   D. 108 ft^2

11. The lateral area of a cylinder is which of the following?

   A. the area of the curved surface.

   B. the total area of the curved surface and one base.

   C. the total area of the curved surface and both bases.

   D. the total area of both bases.

12. What is the lateral area of a cylinder with a radius of 8 feet and a height of 14 feet? ($LA = 2\pi rh$)

   A.   56π ft^2

   B. 112π ft^2

   C. 224π ft^2

   D. 448π ft^2

13. What is the approximate lateral area of a cylinder with a diameter of 10 centimeters and a height of 9 centimeters? ($LA = 2\pi rh$)

   A. 141 cm^2

   B. 283 cm^2

   C. 361 cm^2

   D. 444 cm^2

14. What is the approximate lateral area of the cylinder shown below? ($LA = 2\pi rh$)

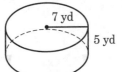

7 yd   5 yd

   A.   70 yd^2

   B. 110 yd^2

   C. 220 yd^2

   D. 440 yd^2

15. A container of oatmeal is in the shape of a cylinder. The height of the container is 7 inches and the diameter is 4 inches. What is the approximate surface area of the container? ($SA = 2\pi rh + 2\pi r^2$)

   A.   25 in.^{2}

   B. 100 in.^{2}

   C. 113 in.^{2}

   D. 276 in.^{2}

16. What is the surface area of a cylinder with a radius of 6 feet and a height of 6 feet? ($SA = 2\pi rh + 2\pi r^2$)

   A.   12π ft^2

   B.   36π ft^2

   C.   72π ft^2

   D. 144π ft^2

17. What is the surface area of a cylinder with a diameter of 10 inches and a height of 4 inches? ($SA = 2\pi rh + 2\pi r^2$)

   A.   90π in.^{2}

   B. 100π in.^{2}

   C. 180π in.^{2}

   D. 280π in.^{2}

18. What is the approximate surface area of the cylinder shown below? ($SA = 2\pi rh + 2\pi r^2$)

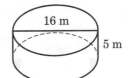

16 m   5 m

   A.   251 m^2

   B.   402 m^2

   C.   653 m^2

   D. 2,110 m^2

Computing Volume of Geometric Figures

LESSON 45

> You will learn how to:
>
> • use formulas to calculate the volume of rectangular prisms and cylinders

Volume is the amount of space enclosed by a three-dimensional object; it is measured in cubic units. The formula for the volume of a rectangular prism is given below.

Volume = (length)(width)(height)

$\qquad V = lwh$

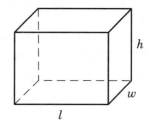

Example: Mandie has a fish tank that measures 20 inches by 12 inches by 10 inches. Find the volume of Mandie's fish tank.

$V = lwh$
$\quad = 20 \cdot 12 \cdot 10$
$\quad = 2,400$

The volume of the fish tank is 2,400 cubic inches.

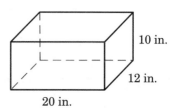

Example: A building with no basement may have a concrete foundation. Find the volume of a foundation 30 feet long, 20 feet wide, and $1\frac{1}{2}$ feet thick.

Thickness is another name for height, so substitute $1\frac{1}{2}$ for h.

$V = lwh$
$V = 30 \cdot 20 \cdot 1\frac{1}{2}$
$V = \frac{30}{1} \cdot \frac{20}{1} \cdot \frac{3}{2}$
$V = 900$

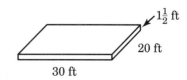

The volume of the foundation is 900 cubic feet.

A cube is a rectangular prism whose length, width, and height are all equal. The volume of a cube whose edge has length s is given by the formula below.

$\qquad V = s^3$

Example: Find the volume of a cube whose edge measures 6 cm.

$V = s^3$
$\quad = 6^3$
$\quad = 216$

The volume is 216 cubic centimeters.

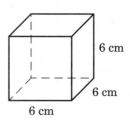

To find the volume of a cylinder, multiply the area of the base by the height. The base of a cylinder is a circle. If the radius of the base is r, the area of the base is πr^2. The formula for the volume of a cylinder is given below.

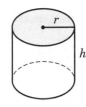

Volume = (base area)(height)

$V = (\pi r^2)(h)$

$V = \pi r^2 h$

Example: Kareem bought a can of car wax that has a radius of 5 centimeters and a height of 10 centimeters. Find the volume of the can of car wax.

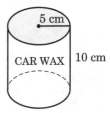

Answer in terms of π	Answer as a decimal approximation
$V = \pi r^2 h$	$V = \pi r^2 h$
$V = \pi(5)^2(10)$	$V \approx (3.14)(5)^2(10)$
$V = 250\pi$	$V \approx 785$

The volume of the can is 250π cm³, or approximately 785 cm³.

Self-Test

Circle the letter of the correct answer.

1. What is the volume the rectangular prism shown below? ($V = lwh$)

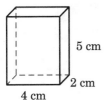

5 cm
2 cm
4 cm

   A. 11 cm³
   B. 33 cm³
   C. 40 cm³
   D. 120 cm³

2. What is the approximate volume of a cylinder with a radius of 3 feet and a height of 10 feet? ($V = \pi r^2 h$)

   A. 30 ft³
   B. 94 ft³
   C. 188 ft³
   D. 283 ft³

Check your answer.

C is correct.

$V = lwh$
$= 4 \cdot 2 \cdot 5$
$= 40$

D is correct.

$V = \pi r^2 h$
$\approx 3.14 \cdot 3^2 \cdot 10$
$\approx 282.6 \approx 283$

Practice

Computing Volume of Geometric Figures

Circle the letter of the correct answer.

1. What is the volume of the rectangular prism shown below? ($V = lwh$)

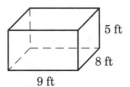

    A. 125 ft³
    B. 360 ft³
    C. 512 ft³
    D. 729 ft³

2. What is the volume of the rectangular prism shown below? ($V = lwh$)

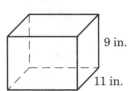

    A.   32 in.³
    B.   132 in.³
    C.   678 in.³
    D. 1,188 in.³

3. What is the volume of a rectangular prism with a length of 2 feet, a width of 8 feet, and a height of 4 feet? ($V = lwh$)

    A.   14 ft³
    B.   40 ft³
    C.   64 ft³
    D. 112 ft³

4. What is the volume of a rectangular prism with a length of 10 centimeters, a width of 5 centimeters, and a height of 6 centimeters? ($V = lwh$)

    A.   21 cm³
    B.   90 cm³
    C. 280 cm³
    D. 300 cm³

5. What is the volume of a rectangular prism with a length of 4.5 feet, a width of 3.9 feet, and a height of 8 feet? ($V = lwh$)

    A.   140.4 ft³
    B.   169.5 ft³
    C. 1,404 ft³
    D. 4,410 ft³

6. What is the volume of the cube shown below? ($V = s^3$)

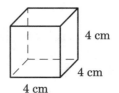

    A. 12 cm³
    B. 16 cm³
    C. 64 cm³
    D. 96 cm³

7. What is the volume of the cube shown below? ($V = s^3$)

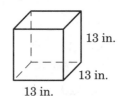

    A.   39 in.³
    B.   169 in.³
    C. 1,014 in.³
    D. 2,197 in.³

8. What is the volume of a cube with an edge that is 2 centimeters long? ($V = s^3$)

    A.   6 cm³
    B.   8 cm³
    C. 12 cm³
    D. 24 cm³

9. What is the volume of a cube with an edge that is 11 yards long? ($V = s^3$)

    A.   121 yd³
    B.   726 yd³
    C. 1,331 yd³
    D. 14,641 yd³

10. What is the volume of a cube with an edge that is 4.5 meters long? ($V = s^3$)

    A.   20.25 m³

    B.   91.125 m³

    C.   121.5 m³

    D. 182.25 m³

11. A floor for a storage shed is 9 feet long, 9 feet wide, and $\frac{1}{2}$ foot thick. What is the volume of the floor? ($V = lwh$)

    A.   20.25 ft³

    B.   40.5 ft³

    C.   81 ft³

    D. 162 ft³

12. A fish pond is shaped like a rectangular prism. It has a length of 10 feet, a width of 8 feet, and a depth of 6 feet. What is the volume of water that the pond can hold? ($V = lwh$)

    A.   24 ft³

    B. 200 ft³

    C. 376 ft³

    D. 480 ft³

13. A block of ice is in the shape of a cube. Each edge is 12 inches long. What is the volume of the block of ice? ($V = s^3$)

    A.   36 in.³

    B.   144 in.³

    C.   864 in.³

    D. 1,728 in.³

14. What is the approximate volume of the cylinder shown below? ($V = \pi r^2 h$)

    A.   51 in.³

    B. 113 in.³

    C. 162 in.³

    D. 509 in.³

15. What is the approximate volume of the cylinder shown below? ($V = \pi r^2 h$)

    A. 1 ft³

    B. 2 ft³

    C. 4 ft³

    D. 6 ft³

16. What is the volume of a cylinder with a radius of 10 meters and a height of 5 meters? ($V = \pi r^2 h$)

    A.   10π m³

    B.   50π m³

    C. 100π m³

    D. 500π m³

17. What is the approximate volume of a cylinder with a radius of 2 centimeters and a height of 3 centimeters? ($V = \pi r^2 h$)

    A. 12 cm³

    B. 24 cm³

    C. 38 cm³

    D. 72 cm³

18. What is the approximate volume of a cylinder with a diameter of 20 centimeters and a height of 10 centimeters? ($V = \pi r^2 h$)

    A.   314 cm³

    B. 3,140 cm³

    C. 6,280 cm³

    D. 12,560 cm³

19. What is the volume of the cylinder shown below? ($V = \pi r^2 h$)

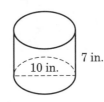

    A.   175π in.³

    B   700π in.³

    C. 1,400π in.³

    D. 2,800π in.³

Estimating and Computing Surface Area and Volume of Irregular Figures

LESSON 46

You will learn how to:

- estimate and compute the surface area and volume of irregular three-dimensional figures

Recall that the surface area of a three-dimensional figure, or solid, is the total area of the outside surface. The volume of a three-dimensional solid is the number of cubic units that will fill the solid. Some figures are considered composite or irregular because they consist of more than one basic figure.

To find the surface area or volume of a composite or irregular three-dimensional solid, follow these steps:

1. Separate the solid into basic geometric solids; it may help to draw extra lines.

2. Add or subtract areas or volumes as needed.

Example: Imagine you want to paint a set of stairs, including the sides, back, and bottom. What is the surface area to be painted?

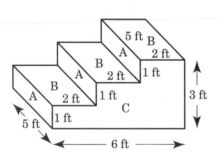

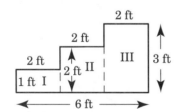

Imagine looking at the stairs from the front. You should see 3 rectangles (A), each 1 foot high and 5 feet wide.

Area of the front view = 3 · (1 · 5) = 15 ft²

Imagine looking at the set of stairs from above. You should see 3 rectangles (B), each 2 feet wide and 5 feet long.

Area of the top view = 3 · (2 · 5) = 30 ft²

Now look at the side view (C).

Draw vertical lines to break it up into 3 rectangles.

Area of rectangle I: 1 × 2 = 2

Area of rectangle II: 2 × 2 = 4

Area of rectangle III: 3 × 2 = 6

Multiply the area of the side view by 2 because the opposite side of the stairs is identical to figure C.

Area of side views = 2(2 + 4 + 6) = 24 ft²

Area of back   = 3 · 5 = 15 ft²

Area of bottom   = 6 · 5 = 30 ft²

Add the areas: 15 + 30 + 24 + 15 + 30 = 114

The surface area to be painted is 114 ft².

Example: Estimate the volume of the stairs.

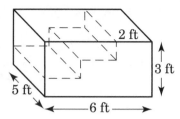

Estimate what part of the entire rectangular prism is filled by the set of stairs. The stairs appear to be more than half of the entire prism. Volume of prism = $lwh = 6 \cdot 5 \cdot 3 = 90$ ft³. $\frac{1}{2}(90) = 45$

So, the volume of the stairs is more than 45 ft³, but less than 90 ft³.

Example: Find the volume of the stairs.

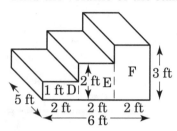

Sections D, E, and F are all rectangular prisms. Find the volume of Section D.
$V = lwh = 5 \cdot 2 \cdot 1 = 10$ ft³
Find the volume of Section E.
$V = lwh = 5 \cdot 2 \cdot 2 = 20$ ft³
Find the volume of Section F.
$V = lwh = 5 \cdot 2 \cdot 3 = 30$ ft³

Add the three volumes: $10 + 20 + 30 = 60$

The volume of the stairs is 60 ft³.

Self-Test

Circle the letter of the correct answer.

1. What is the surface area of the solid?

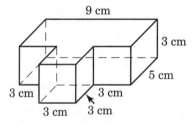

A. 162 cm²

B. 210 cm²

C. 219 cm²

D. 228 cm²

2. What is the volume of the solid? (The top of the solid is half of a cylinder)

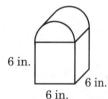

A. 243π in.³

B. 216π in.³

C. $(216 + 27\pi)$ in.³

D. $(180 + 36\pi)$ in.³

Check your answer.

B is correct.

Divide the solid into a large rectangular prism and a small cube. Find the areas on the outside and add.

rectangular prism:
SA = 2(9 · 5) + 2(3 · 5) + 9 · 3 + 2(3 · 3) = 165

cube: SA = 5(3 × 3) = 45
165 + 45 = 210

The total surface area of the solid is 210 cm².

C is correct.

Cube: V = s³ = 6³ = 216

Half-cylinder: V = $\frac{1}{2}(\pi r^2 h) = \frac{1}{2}(\pi \cdot 3^2 \cdot 6)$
= 27π

The volume of the solid is (216 + 27π) in.³

Practice

Estimating and Computing Surface Area and Volume of Irregular Figures

Circle the letter of the correct answer.

1. What is the surface area of the solid?

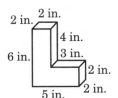

A. 40 in.²

B. 62 in.²

C. 70 in.²

D. 80 in.²

2. What is the surface area of the solid?

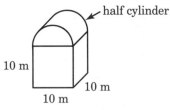

A. (500 + 75π)m²

B. (600 + 75π)m²

C. (500 + 150π)m²

D. (600 + 150π)m²

3. What is the surface area of the solid?

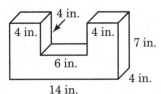

A. 348 in.²

B. 380 in.²

C. 400 in.²

D. 412 in.²

4. What is the surface area of the solid?

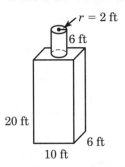

A. (760 + 24π)ft²

B. (760 + 28π)ft²

C. (1,200 + 24π)ft²

D. (1,200 + 28π)ft²

5. Which is the best estimate for the volume of the solid?

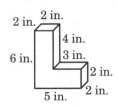

A. less than 12 in.³

B. between 12 in.³ and 24 in.³

C. between 24 in.³ and 60 in.³

D. more than 60 in.³

6. Which is the best estimate for the volume of the solid, in cubic feet?

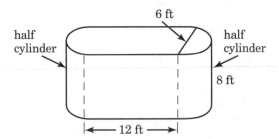

A. less than 480

B. between 480 and 576

C. between 576 and 864

D. more than 864

7. Which is the best estimate for the volume of the solid?

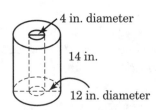

A. less than 400π in.³

B. between 400π in.³ and 500π in.³

C. between 500π in.³ and 600π in.³

D. more than 600π in.³

8. Which is the best estimate for the volume of the solid?

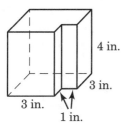

4 in.

3 in.

3 in.

1 in.

A. less than 50 in.³
B. between 50 in.³ and 62 in.³
C. between 62 in.³ and 70 in.³
D. more than 70 in.³

9. What is the volume of the solid?

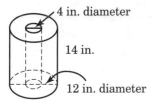

4 in. diameter

14 in.

12 in. diameter

A. about 879 in.³
B. about 1,407 in.³
C. about 1,758 in.³
D. about 5,627 in.³

10. What is the volume of the solid?

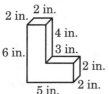

2 in.   2 in.
2 in.
4 in.
6 in.   3 in.
2 in.
2 in.
5 in.

A. 36 in.³
B. 40 in.³
C. 48 in.³
D. 66 in.³

11. What is the volume of the solid?

half cylinder

10 m

10 m

10 m

A. (100 + 125π) m³
B. (100 + 150π) m³
C. (1,000 + 125π) m³
D. (1,000 + 150π) m³

12. What is the volume of the solid?

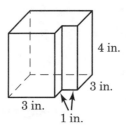

4 in.

3 in.

3 in.

1 in.

A. 48 in.³
B. 60 in.³
C. 80 in.³
D. 92 in.³

13. What is the volume of the solid?

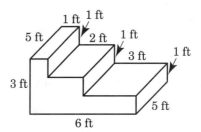

1 ft   1 ft
5 ft   2 ft   1 ft
3 ft
3 ft
5 ft
6 ft

A. 40 ft³
B. 50 ft³
C. 60 ft³
D. 90 ft³

14. What is the volume of the solid?

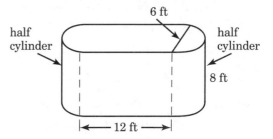

6 ft

half cylinder

half cylinder

8 ft

12 ft

A. (576 + 72π) ft³
B. (576 + 144π) ft³
C. (576 + 288π) ft³
D. (576 + 576π) ft³

Computing Measurements of Rectangular Prisms Based on Dimensional Changes

LESSON 47

You will learn how to:
- determine and apply ratios of surface areas and volumes of similar rectangular prisms

Key Words: ratio, similar, scale factor

You know that a *ratio* is a comparison of two numbers by division. There are different ways to write and read a ratio. The ratio $\frac{3}{4}$ can also be written "3:4" and read "3 to 4."

Three-dimensional figures are *similar* if they have the same shape and the ratios of all corresponding dimensions are equal.

Example: Are the figures similar?

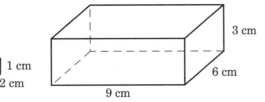

Find the ratios of all corresponding dimensions.

	Prism 1	Prism 2	Ratio
length	3	9	3:9 or 1:3
width	2	6	2:6 or 1:3
height	1	3	1:3

The figures are similar because they are the same shape, and the ratios of all corresponding dimensions are 1:3. The ratio 1:3 is called the *scale factor*.

Example: Find the ratio of surface areas of the prisms in the example above.

Prism 1
$SA = 2lw + 2lh + 2wh$
$= 2 \cdot 3 \cdot 2 + 2 \cdot 3 \cdot 1 + 2 \cdot 2 \cdot 1$
$= 12 + 6 + 4$
$= 22 \text{ cm}^2$

Prism 2
$SA = 2lw + 2lh + 2wh$
$= 2 \cdot 9 \cdot 6 + 2 \cdot 9 \cdot 3 + 2 \cdot 6 \cdot 3$
$= 108 + 54 + 36$
$= 198 \text{ cm}^2$

The ratio of the surface area of Prism 1 to that of Prism 2 is 22:198, or 1:9. Note that the scale factor is 1:3, and the ratio of the surface areas is 1:9, or $1^2:3^2$.

If the scale factor of two similar figures is $a:b$, then the ratio of their surface areas is $a^2:b^2$, or the square of the scale factor.

Example: If the scale factor of two cubes is 3:4, what is the ratio of their surface areas?

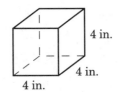

Scale factor $= 3:4$
Ratio of surface areas $= 3^2 : 4^2 = 9:16$

Example: Find the ratio of the volumes of the rectangular prisms.

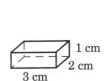 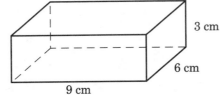

1 cm
2 cm
3 cm

3 cm
6 cm
9 cm

Prism 1
$V = lwh$
$= 3 \cdot 2 \cdot 1$
$= 6 \text{ in.}^3$

Prism 2
$V = lwh$
$= 9 \cdot 6 \cdot 3$
$= 162 \text{ in.}^3$

The ratio of the volume of Prism 1 to that of Prism 2 is $6:162$, or $1:27$. Note that the scale factor is $1:3$, and the ratio of the volumes is $1:27$, or $1^3:3^3$.

If the scale factor of two similar three-dimensional figures is $a:b$, then the ratio of their volumes is $a^3:b^3$, or the cube of the scale factor.

Example: Two prisms are similar with a scale factor of $1:5$. If the volume of the smaller prism is 20 in.^3, what is the volume of the larger prism?

The scale factor is $1:5$. The ratio of the volumes is $1^3:5^3$, or $1:125$. Let v represent the volume of the larger prism and write a proportion to solve the problem.

$$\frac{\text{volume of smaller prism}}{\text{volume of larger prism}} \rightarrow \frac{1}{125} = \frac{20}{v}$$
$$v = 2,500$$

The volume of the larger prism is $2,500 \text{ in.}^3$

Self-Test

Circle the letter of the correct answer.

1. The edge of a cube is twice the edge of a smaller cube. What is the ratio of the surface area of the smaller cube to that of the larger cube?

   A. 1:2   C. 1:6

   B. 1:4   D. 1:8

2. The scale factor of two similar prisms is $1:4$. If the volume of the larger prism is 192 ft^3, what is the volume of the smaller prism?

   A. 3 ft³   C. 16 ft³

   B. 6 ft³   D. 48 ft³

Check your answer.

B is correct.

The scale factor is $1:2$, so the ratio of the surface areas is $1^2:2^2$, or $1:4$.

A is correct.

The ratio of the volumes is the cube of the scale factor. $1^3:4^3 = 1:64$. Let v represent the volume of the smaller prism.

$$\frac{\text{volume of smaller prism}}{\text{volume of larger prism}} \rightarrow \frac{1}{64} = \frac{v}{192}$$
$$v = 3$$

Practice

Computing Measurements of Rectangular Prisms Based on Dimensional Changes

Circle the letter of the correct answer.

1. A rectangular prism is 6 centimeters long, 4 centimeters wide, and 5 centimeters high. Which prism is similar to it?

   A. 12 cm long, 6 cm wide, 10 cm high
   B. 12 cm long, 8 cm wide, 10 cm high
   C. 18 cm long, 8 cm wide, 10 cm high
   D. 18 cm long, 12 cm wide, 10 cm high

2. An edge of a cube is 4 times the edge of a smaller cube. What is the ratio of the surface area of the smaller cube to that of the larger cube?

   A. 1:4
   B. 1:8
   C. 1:16
   D. 1:24

3. The scale factor for two similar prisms is 1:9. What is the ratio of their surface areas?

   A. 1:3
   B. 1:18
   C. 1:27
   D. 1:81

4. The scale factor of two similar prisms is 2:3. If the surface area of the larger prism is 72 in.^{2}, what is the surface area of the smaller prism?

   A. 18 in.^{2}
   B. 24 in.^{2}
   C. 32 in.^{2}
   D. 36 in.^{2}

5. One edge of a prism measures 2 cm. The corresponding edge of a similar prism measures 3 cm. What is the ratio of the surface areas of the prisms?

   A. 2:3
   B. 4:6
   C. 4:9
   D. 6:9

6. The scale factor of two similar prisms is 1:4. If the surface area of the larger prism is 96 m^2, what is the surface area of the smaller prism?

   A. 6 m^2
   B. 16 m^2
   C. 24 m^2
   D. 48 m^2

7. The scale factor for two cubes is 6:5. What is the ratio of their surface areas?

   A. 36:25
   B. 12:10
   C. 30:25
   D. 36:30

8. One edge of a prism measures 3 cm. The corresponding edge of a similar prism measures 5 cm. If the surface area of the smaller prism is 36 in.^{2}, what is the surface area of the larger prism?

   A. 60 in.^{2}
   B. 100 in.^{2}
   C. 108 in.^{2}
   D. 180 in.^{2}

9. The scale factor of two cubes is 1:4. If the surface area of the smaller cube is 10 yd², what is the surface area of the larger cube?

    A. 16 yd²
    B. 40 yd²
    C. 64 yd²
    D. 160 yd²

10. The ratio of the surface areas of two similar prisms is 81:4. What is the ratio of their corresponding edges?

    A. 9:2
    B. 9:16
    C. 18:2
    D. 18:16

11. A cube is 1 centimeter on each edge. The length of each edge of the cube is doubled. What happens to the volume of the cube?

    A. The volume is doubled.
    B. The volume is tripled.
    C. The volume is multiplied by 6.
    D. The volume is multiplied by 8.

12. By what number is the volume of a prism multiplied if the length, width and height of the prism are tripled?

    A. 3
    B. 6
    C. 9
    D. 27

13. One edge of a prism measures 1 in. The corresponding edge of a similar prism measures 8 in. What is the ratio of the volumes of the prisms?

    A. 1:2
    B. 1:64
    C. 1:256
    D. 1:512

14. The scale factor for two similar prisms is 4:3. What is the ratio of their volumes?

    A. 12:9
    B. 16:9
    C. 64:27
    D. 8:6

15. One edge of a cube measures 10 cm. An edge of another cube measures 9 cm. What is the ratio of the volumes of the cubes?

    A. 100:81
    B. 1,000:729
    C. 30:27
    D. 1,000:900

16. The ratio of the volumes of two similar prisms is 27:125. What is the ratio of their surface areas?

    A. 3:5
    B. 9:25
    C. 15:45
    D. 9:15

17. The scale factor of two similar prisms is 3:2. If the volume of the larger prism is 54 ft³, what is the volume of the smaller prism?

    A. 16 ft³
    B. 24 ft³
    C. 36 ft³
    D. 48 ft³

18. The scale factor of two cubes is 2:5. If the volume of the smaller cube is 40 cm³, what is the volume of the larger cube?

    A. 100 cm³
    B. 250 cm³
    C. 500 cm³
    D. 625 cm³

Applying the Pythagorean Theorem

L E S S O N   4 8

You will learn how to:

- use the Pythagorean theorem to find the missing side of a right triangle

- use the Pythagorean theorem to find the length of a line segment in the coordinate plane

- use the converse of the Pythagorean theorem to determine if a triangle is a right triangle

Key Words: right triangle, legs, hypotenuse, Pythagorean theorem

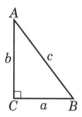

If a triangle has a right angle (90°), then it is a **_right triangle_**. The two sides of the triangle that form the right angle are called the **_legs_**. Side AC and side BC are the legs of this right triangle. The side opposite the right angle is called the **_hypotenuse_**, and it is always the longest side of the triangle. The hypotenuse of this right triangle is side AB.

The **_Pythagorean theorem_** states that in a right triangle, the sum of the squares of the lengths of the legs equals the square of the length of the hypotenuse. If a and b are the lengths of the legs and c is the length of the hypotenuse, then $a^2 + b^2 = c^2$.

If you know the lengths of any two sides of a right triangle, you can use the Pythagorean theorem to find the length of the third side.

Example: Find the length of the missing side.

The missing side is the hypotenuse of the right triangle.

$$3^2 + 4^2 = x^2$$
$$9 + 16 = x^2$$
$$25 = x^2$$
$$\sqrt{25} = x$$
$$5 = x$$

The missing side is 5 units long.

Example: Find the length of the missing side.

The missing side is one of the legs of the right triangle.

$$a^2 + 10^2 = 12^2$$
$$a^2 + 100 = 144$$
$$a^2 = 44$$
$$a = \sqrt{44}$$
$$a = \sqrt{4} \cdot \sqrt{11}$$
$$a = 2\sqrt{11}$$

The missing side is $2\sqrt{11}$ cm long.

Example: Find the length of the line segment connecting points $(-1, 8)$ and $(7, 2)$.

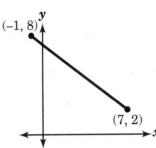

You can form a right triangle by drawing segments PR and QR. By counting units on the coordinate system, you can see that $PR = 6$ and $QR = 8$. The length you need to find is the hypotenuse of the right triangle, whose length is r.

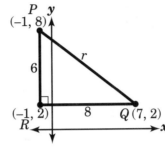

$$6^2 + 8^2 = r^2$$
$$36 + 64 = r^2$$
$$100 = r^2$$
$$\sqrt{100} = r$$
$$10 = r$$

The length of the segment is 10 units.

The converse of the Pythagorean theorem states that if $a^2 + b^2 = c^2$, then a, b, and c are lengths of the sides of a right triangle.

Example:

The sides of a triangle have lengths of 12, 13, and 5. Is the triangle a right triangle?

$$5^2 + 12^2 \overset{?}{=} 13^2$$
$$25 + 144 \overset{?}{=} 169$$
$$169 = 169$$

It is a right triangle.

Example:

The sides of a triangle have lengths of 7, 10, and 8. Is the triangle a right triangle?

$$7^2 + 8^2 \overset{?}{=} 10^2$$
$$49 + 64 \overset{?}{=} 100$$
$$113 \neq 100$$

It is not a right triangle.

Self-Test

Circle the letter of the correct answer.

Find the length of the line segment connecting points $(-1, -3)$ and $(4, 0)$.

A. 4

B. $\sqrt{34}$

C. $2\sqrt{17}$

D. 8

Check your answer.

B is correct.

The segment connecting the points is the hypotenuse of a right triangle whose legs have lengths 5 and 3.

$$5^2 + 3^2 = c^2$$
$$25 + 9 = c^2$$
$$34 = c^2$$
$$\sqrt{34} = c$$

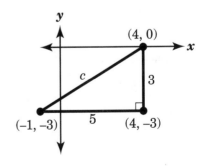

Practice

Applying the Pythagorean Theorem

Circle the letter of the correct answer.

1. Find the length of the missing side.

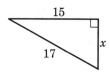

A. 2
B. 8
C. 16
D. 64

2. Find the length of the line segment joining points (3, 1) and (11, 7).

A. 6
B. 8
C. 10
D. 12

3. Find the value of x so that 15, 20, and x are the lengths of the sides of a right triangle and x is the length of the longest side.

A. 25
B. 35
C. 40
D. 60

4. The lengths of the shorter sides of a right triangle are 7 and 24. What is the length of the longest side?

A. 25
B. 36
C. 49
D. 64

5. Find the length of the missing side.

A. 8
B. 10
C. 15
D. 20

6. The lengths of the legs of a right triangle are 9 and 12. What is the length of the hypotenuse?

A. 15
B. 17
C. 20
D. 25

7. What is the value of p in the triangle shown below?

A. 7
B. 10
C. 12
D. 13

8. What is the distance d?

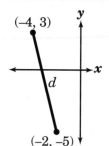

A. $\sqrt{6}$
B. $\sqrt{10}$
C. $2\sqrt{15}$
D. $2\sqrt{17}$

9. Find the value of x so that x, 24, and 25 are the lengths of the sides of a right triangle and x is the length of the shortest side.

A. 1
B. 7
C. 9
D. 13

10. What is the distance between the points (3, 6) and (9, −2)?

A. $\sqrt{10}$
B. $2\sqrt{7}$
C. 10
D. 14

11. Find the length of the missing side.

- A. 9
- B. $9\sqrt{2}$
- C. 12
- D. $90\sqrt{2}$

12. Find the value of x so that 8, 15, and x are the lengths of the sides of a right triangle and x is the length of the longest side.

- A. 15
- B. 17
- C. 20
- D. 25

13. What is the value of z in the triangle shown below?

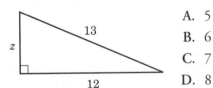

- A. 5
- B. 6
- C. 7
- D. 8

14. The hypotenuse of a right triangle is 26. One leg is 24. Find the other leg.

- A. 8
- B. 10
- C. 15
- D. 20

15. What is the distance between the points $(5, 0)$ and $(0, -12)$?

- A. $\sqrt{13}$
- B. $\sqrt{119}$
- C. 13
- D. 17

16. The legs of a right triangle are 12 and 16. What is the length of the hypotenuse?

- A. 17
- B. 18
- C. 19
- D. 20

17. Find the length of the line segment joining points $(2, 6)$ and $(6, 2)$.

- A. $\sqrt{8}$
- B. 4
- C. $4\sqrt{2}$
- D. 8

18. The hypotenuse of a right triangle is $8\sqrt{2}$. One leg is 8. Find the other leg.

- A. 5
- B. 6
- C. 7
- D. 8

19. The hypotenuse of a right triangle is 25. One leg is 24. Find the other leg.

- A. 5
- B. 7
- C. 10
- D. 12

20. Find the value of x so that x, 28, and 35 are the lengths of the sides of a right triangle and x is the length of the shortest side.

- A. 21
- B. 23
- C. 25
- D. 30

Identifying Congruent Figures and Their Parts

LESSON 49

You will learn how to:
- identify congruent figures and their corresponding parts

Key Words: congruent, corresponding parts

Congruent figures have the same shape and size. Two polygons are congruent if and only if their vertices can be matched so that corresponding angles and sides are equal in measure. The symbol ≅ means "is congruent to."

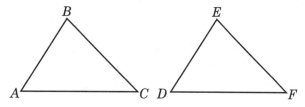

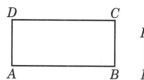

△*ABC* and △*DEF* are the same size and shape. △*ABC* ≅ △*DEF*

Polygon *ABCD* is the same shape as polygon *EFGH*, but they are not the same size. They are not congruent.

The pairs of matching sides and angles of two polygons are called *corresponding parts.* If two polygons are congruent, all pairs of corresponding parts are equal in measure, or congruent.

These triangles are congruent. Their congruent corresponding parts are indicated by identical marks.

Pairs of congruent angles   Pairs of congruent sides

$\angle L \cong \angle R$, $\angle M \cong \angle S$, $\angle N \cong \angle Q$ $\overline{LM} \cong \overline{RS}$, $\overline{MN} \cong \overline{SQ}$, $\overline{NL} \cong \overline{QR}$

When naming congruent polygons, the corresponding vertices must be in the same order.   →   △*LMN* ≅ △*RSQ*

Example: Complete the congruence statement.
            ABCD ≅ _____

To get the correct order of vertices, match the identical marks on the angles.
∠*A* corresponds to ∠*F*, ∠*B* corresponds to ∠*E*, and so on.

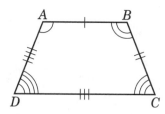

ABCD ≅ *FEHG*

You can use three letters to name an angle. For example, ∠*A* can also be named ∠*DAB* or ∠*BAD*.

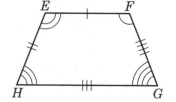

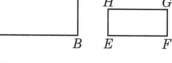

If there are no markings on the diagram, you can name corresponding parts of congruent polygons by referring to the congruence statement.

Example: $\overline{TU} \cong$ _____   Find the vertices that match T and U.

$$\downarrow\ \downarrow \qquad \downarrow\ \downarrow$$
$$\triangle\ T\ U\ V \cong \triangle\ W\ X\ Y$$
$$\overline{TU} \cong \overline{WX}$$

$\triangle TUV \cong \triangle WXY$

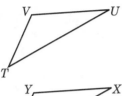

$\overline{VT} \cong$ _____   Find the vertices that match V and T.

$$\downarrow \qquad \downarrow \qquad \downarrow \qquad \downarrow$$
$$\triangle\ T\ U\ V \cong \triangle\ W\ X\ Y$$
$$\overline{VT} \cong \overline{YW}$$

$\angle U \cong$ _____   Find the vertex that matches U.

$$\downarrow \qquad\qquad\qquad \downarrow$$
$$\triangle\ T\ U\ V \cong \triangle\ W\ X\ Y$$
$$\angle U \cong \angle X$$

If $m\angle V = 110°$ what is $m\angle Y$? $\angle Y$ is congruent to $\angle V$, so they have the same measure.   The measure of $\angle Y$ is 110°.

Example: $\angle N \cong$ _____   Find the vertex that matches N.

$$\downarrow \qquad\qquad \downarrow$$
$$H\ I\ J\ K \cong O\ N\ M\ P$$
$$\angle N \cong \angle I$$

$HIJK \cong ONMP$

$\overline{JH} \cong$ _____   Find the vertices that match J and H.

$$\downarrow\ \downarrow \qquad \downarrow\ \downarrow$$
$$H\ I\ J\ K \cong O\ N\ M\ P$$
$$\overline{JH} \cong \overline{MO}$$

Self-Test

Circle the letter of the correct answer.

$\triangle ABC \cong \triangle XYZ$. $AB = 3$; $BC = 4$; $AC = 5$. What is YZ?

A. 3   C. 5
B. 4   D. 7

Check your answer.

B is correct.
The order of the vertices of the triangles in the congruence statement indicates which sides are congruent. Because $\overline{YZ} \cong \overline{BC}$, they have the same length.

Practice

Identifying Congruent Figures and Their Parts

Circle the letter of the correct answer.

1. Which statement correctly names the pair of congruent figures?

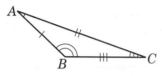

A. $\triangle ABC \cong \triangle JHI$
B. $\triangle ABC \cong \triangle HIJ$
C. $\triangle ABC \cong \triangle HJI$
D. $\triangle ABC \cong \triangle JIH$

2. $\overline{BC} \cong$ ____

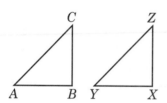

$\triangle ABC \cong \triangle YXZ$

A. $\overline{XZ}$
B. $\overline{YZ}$
C. $\overline{YX}$
D. $\overline{ZY}$

3. $QR =$

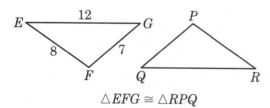

$\triangle EFG \cong \triangle RPQ$

A. 7
B. 8
C. 12
D. 15

4. Which statement correctly names the pair of congruent figures?

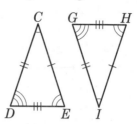

A. $\triangle CDE \cong \triangle IHG$
B. $\triangle CDE \cong \triangle GHI$
C. $\triangle CDE \cong \triangle IGH$
D. $\triangle CDE \cong \triangle GIH$

5. $\angle B \cong$ ____

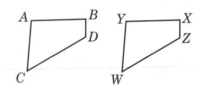

$ABDC \cong YXZW$

A. $\angle Z$
B. $\angle W$
C. $\angle Y$
D. $\angle X$

6. $\overline{PN} \cong$ ____

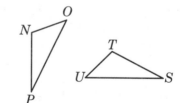

$\triangle NOP \cong \triangle TUS$

A. $\overline{ST}$
B. $\overline{TU}$
C. $\overline{ON}$
D. $\overline{SU}$

7. $m\angle J = 82°$, $m\angle K = 74°$, and $m\angle L = 24°$. What is the measure of $\angle U$?

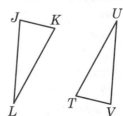

A. 24°
B. 74°
C. 82°
D. 90°

$\triangle JKL \cong \triangle VTU$

Lesson 49: Identifying Congruent Figures and Their Parts

8. Which statement correctly names the pair of congruent figures?

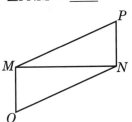

- A. $WXYZ \cong EFCD$
- B. $WXYZ \cong DEFC$
- C. $WXYZ \cong DCEF$
- D. $WXYZ \cong CDEF$

9. $\angle PNM \cong$ ____

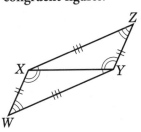

- A. $\angle NOM$
- B. $\angle OMN$
- C. $\angle MNO$
- D. $\angle ONM$

$\triangle MNO \cong \triangle NMP$

10. $\triangle ABC \cong \triangle LMN$. $\overline{ML} \cong$ ____

- A. $\overline{AC}$
- B. $\overline{BC}$
- C. $\overline{CB}$
- D. $\overline{BA}$

11. Which statement correctly names the pair of congruent figures?

- A. $\triangle WXY \cong \triangle ZYX$
- B. $\triangle WXY \cong \triangle ZXY$
- C. $\triangle WXY \cong \triangle YXZ$
- D. $\triangle WXY \cong \triangle YZX$

12. $\triangle GHI \cong \triangle RST$. $GH = 10$, $HI = 25.6$, and $GI = 19$. $ST =$

- A. 10
- B. 19
- C. 25.6
- D. 29

13. $MG =$

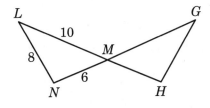

$\triangle LMN \cong \triangle GMH$

- A. 2
- B. 6
- C. 8
- D. 10

14. $\triangle ABC \cong \triangle XYZ$. $\overline{YZ} \cong$ ____

- A. $\overline{BC}$
- B. $\overline{XY}$
- C. $\overline{AC}$
- D. $\overline{AB}$

15. $ABCD \cong WXYZ$. $\angle Y \cong$ ____

- A. $\angle A$
- B. $\angle B$
- C. $\angle C$
- D. $\angle D$

16. $\triangle BCD \cong \triangle RST$. $m\angle B = 54.2°$, $m\angle C = 80°$, and $m\angle D = 45.8°$. What is the measure of $\angle T$?

- A. 45.8°
- B. 54.2°
- C. 80°
- D. 100°

Computing Mean, Median, and Mode

LESSON 50

> You will learn how to:
> - find the mean, median, and mode of a data set
>
> **Key Words:** data, element, mean, median, mode

A company has two secretaries that each earn $20,000 a year, three part-time technicians that each earn $17,000 a year, a computer specialist that earns $28,000 a year, and an office manager that earns $30,000 a year. The president earns $700,000 a year and the vice-president earns $150,000 a year.

The salaries are called *data* because they are items of information. Each item of information in a set of data is called an *element* of the set.

Three measures that can be used to describe a set of data are mean, median, and mode.

To find the *mean* of a data set, add the data elements and divide the sum by the number of elements in the data set.

mean = (sum of the elements) ÷ (number of elements)

Example: Find the mean salary of the company employees.

mean = (sum of the salaries) ÷ (number of salaries)

mean = (20,000 + 20,000 + 17,000 + 17,000 + 17,000
        + 28,000 + 30,000 + 700,000 + 150,000) ÷ 9

mean = (999,000) ÷ 9 = 111,000

The mean salary is $111,000.

Another measure that can be used to describe a set of data is the median. The *median* of a set of data is the middle element when the data are arranged in increasing or decreasing order.

Example: Find the median salary of the company
                 employees.

Rewrite the data in order from least to greatest:

   17,000; 17,000; 17,000; 20,000; 20,000; 28,000; 30,000; 150,000; 700,000

Find the middle number:

   17,000; 17,000; 17,000; 20,000; **20,000**; 28,000; 30,000; 150,000; 700,000

The median salary is $20,000.

If the number of elements in a data set is even, there is no middle element. To find the median of a data set with an even number of elements, find the mean of the 2 middle elements.

Example: Find the median of 1, 8, 9, 10, 1, and 3.

Rewrite the data in order from least to greatest: 1, 1, 3, 8, 9, 10
Find the 2 middle elements: 1, 1, <u>3, 8</u>, 9, 10
Find the mean of the two middle elements: $(3 + 8) \div 2 = (11) \div 2 = 5.5$
The median is 5.5.

A third measure that can be used to describe a set of data is the mode.
The *mode* of a data set is the element that appears most often.
A data set can have no mode, one mode, or more than one mode.

Example: Find the mode of the salaries of the company employees.

Find the element that appears most often in the set.
20,000, 20,000, 17,000, 17,000, 17,000, 28,000, 30,000, 700,000, 150,000
17,000 appears the most often. The mode is $17,000.

Example: Find the mode of 18, 6, 23, 14, 6, 7, 9, and 14.

Both 6 and 14 appear twice. The modes are 6 and 14.

Example: Find the mode of 23, 49, 94, 50, 36, and 15.

All of the elements appear once in the data set. There is no mode.

Self-Test

Circle the letter of the correct answer.

What is Giselle's mean test score?

	Test 1	Test 2	Test 3
Hanna	86	86	86
Giselle	81	75	99
Paul	100	91	91

A. 85
B. 86
C. 89
D. 94

Check your answer.

A is correct.

Giselle's test scores are 81, 75, and 99.
mean = (81 + 75 + 99) ÷ 3 = 255 ÷ 3 = 85
Her mean test score is 85.

Practice

Computing Mean, Median, and Mode

Circle the letter of the correct answer.

1. Find the mean of 6, 5, 16, 18, 14, 4, 20, 13, 9, and 5.

   A. 9
   B. 10
   C. 11
   D. 12

2. What is the median of 15, 13, 6, 20, 15, 13, 1, 5, and 7?

   A. 13
   B. 15
   C. 16
   D. 20

3. Find the mode of 11, 18, 7, 18, 20, 16, 19, 19, 14, 8, and 9.

   A. 16
   B. 18
   C. 18 and 19
   D. 19

4. Mr. Lawrence made a list of the number of books his students read last summer:
   3, 10, 2, 13, 19, 20, 6, 12, 13, 6, 17.
   What is the median number of books read?

   A. 6
   B. 11
   C. 12
   D. 20

5. Find the median of 19, 18, 23, 44, 36, and 29.

   A. 26.0
   B. 27.0
   C. 28.2
   D. 33.5

6. What is the mode of 73, 49, 93, 44, 85, 39, 81, 84, 29, and 93?

   A. 67
   B. 77
   C. 93
   D. 100

7. Find the mode of 188, 125, 193, 144, and 108.

   A. none
   B. 144
   C. 188
   D. 193

8. Paul recorded the following thermometer readings one week:
   33, 40, 33, 34, 38, 32.
   Find the mean.

   A. 33
   B. 35
   C. 37
   D. 38

9. Find the median of 94, 77, 48, 48, 88, and 62.

   A. 58.5
   B. 67.7
   C. 69.5
   D. 77.5

10. What is the mean of 10.1, 35.9, and 10.1?

    A. 15.7
    B. 16.2
    C. 17.4
    D. 18.7

Lesson 50: Computing Mean, Median, and Mode

11. What is the mean of 62, 86, 21, and 79?

A. 61
B. 62
C. 63
D. 64

12. What is the median of the following numbers?
5.2, 22.6, 31.9, 14.7, 19.5, 24.7

A. 16.5
B. 19.2
C. 21.05
D. 21.15

13. Several students compared how long they studied for a big test. Their times, in hours, were 13, 13, 0, 10, 6, and 12. What was the median time?

A. 5 hours
B. 9 hours
C. 10 hours
D. 11 hours

14. What is the mode of 14, 14, 11, 6, 8, and 9?

A. 8.5
B. 10
C. 10.3
D. 14

15. What is the mean number of sales for Monday?

SALES TABLE

	Monday	Wednesday
Anna	14	19
Bailey	30	27
Chris	16	20
David	8	10
Eric	28	25

A. 8
B. 16
C. 19.2
D. 24

16. Find the mode of 231, 445, 297, 249, 170, 239, 220, 445, and 216.

A. none
B. 239
C. 279.1
D. 445

17. What is the mode of 263, 152, 166, and 314?

A. none
B. 166
C. 166 and 263
D. 263

18. Find the median of 31.6, 48, 18.7, 32.6, 49.2, 48.8, 35, 26.2, 13.8, and 10.

A. 32.1
B. 35
C. 49
D. 49.2

19. What is the median number of cars in the garages?

	Cars	Trucks
Garage 1	2	0
Garage 2	15	0
Garage 3	23	5
Garage 4	6	2
Garage 5	1	8

A. 4
B. 6
C. 9.4
D. 23

20. Hector polled his neighbors to find out how many pets they have. Here are the results:
0, 3, 2, 0, 1, 1, 7, 2, 4, 10
What is the mean number of pets?

A. 1 and 0
B. 2
C. 3
D. 10

Lesson 50: Computing Mean, Median, and Mode

Identifying Elements of a Data Set

LESSON 51

You will learn how to:

• find the minimum, lower quartile, upper quartile, and maximum of a data set

Key Words: minimum, maximum, lower quartile, upper quartile

Jackie recorded the test scores of eleven students in her science class. The scores were 63, 70, 86, 80, 85, 71, 65, 72, 81, 89, and 62. Jackie knows that if she writes the scores in numerical order, the middle score is the median. What are some other measures that can be used to describe the set of scores?

The *minimum* is the least value in a data set.

The *maximum* is the greatest value in a data set.

If the elements of a data set are written in increasing order, the median forms two subsets.

The *lower quartile* is the median of the lower subset.

The *upper quartile* is the median of the upper subset.

Example: Find the minimum, lower quartile, median, upper quartile, and maximum of the test scores.

Write the scores in increasing order. The answers are shown below:

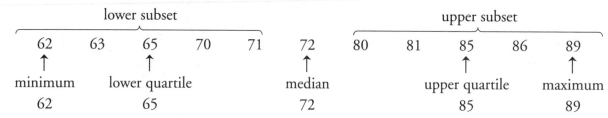

This data set has 11 elements. The lower quartile is the median of the lower 5 scores, and the upper quartile is the median of the upper 5 scores.

Example: Find the minimum, lower quartile, median, upper quartile, and maximum of {7, 2, 2, 5, 12, 9, 9, 12, 2, 13, 2, 6, 10, 12}.

Because there are two elements in the middle, the median is the mean of those two elements. median = $(7 + 9) \div 2 = 8$

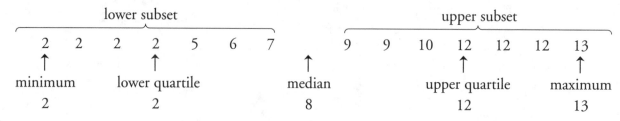

Example: Find the minimum, lower quartile, median, upper quartile, and maximum of {2, 13, 20, 3, 19, 18, 6, 19}.

Because there are two elements in the middle, the median is the mean of those two elements.   median = (13 + 18) ÷ 2 = 15.5

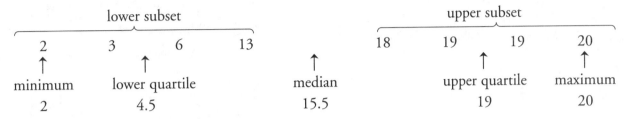

lower subset
2   3   6   13
↑   ↑
minimum   lower quartile
2   4.5

median
↑
15.5

upper subset
18   19   19   20
            ↑   ↑
      upper quartile   maximum
            19   20

This data set has 8 elements. The lower quartile is the median of the lower 4 elements, and the upper quartile is the median of the upper 4 elements.

You can see that for this data set, the lower quartile is also a mean because there are two elements in the middle of the lower subset.

lower quartile = (3 + 6) ÷ 2 = 4.5

Self-Test

Circle the letter of the correct answer.

What is upper quartile value of the set?

{219, 305, 245, 170, 333, 245, 260}

A. 219

B. 245

C. 305

D. 333

Check your answer.

C is correct.

Put the list in order from least to greatest and identify the median: 170, 219, 245, 245, 260, 305, 333.

The median divides the list into two subsets of three elements each. Find the median of the upper subset.
260, 305, 333

Practice

Identifying Elements of a Data Set

Circle the letter of the correct answer.

1. Find the minimum value of the data.
   {4, 6, 3, 14, 10, 10, 16, 10, 16}

   A. 1
   B. 3
   C. 10
   D. 16

2. What is the median of the data?
   {17, 0, 19, 12, 6, 3, 3, 16, 2, 16, 18}

   A. 3
   B. 12
   C. 14
   D. 17

3. Find the lower quartile value of the data.
   {4, 10, 8, 19, 19, 7, 11}

   A. 7
   B. 8
   C. 10
   D. 19

4. Several students compared how many letters
   they mailed last summer. The results were
   13, 14, 17, 8, 10, 16, 0, 17, 0, and 10.
   What is the maximum value of the data?

   A. 10
   B. 16
   C. 17
   D. 18

5. Find the upper quartile value of the data.
   {17, 1, 13, 20, 1, 9, 8, 1, 15, 8, 1}

   A. 8
   B. 13
   C. 15
   D. 20

6. A company has forty employees. The upper
   quartile of the salaries of the employees is
   the median of

   A. the top ten salaries
   B. the top twenty salaries
   C. the middle twenty salaries
   D. all forty salaries

7. Find the minimum.
   {5.0, 4.8, 3.4, 9.0, 5.7, 2.1, 9.6, 1.3}

   A. 1.3
   B. 2.1
   C. 3.4
   D. 9.6

8. Find the median.
   {4.5, 6.1, 7.5, 3.1, 4.7, 7.4, 6.4, 5.4}

   A. 3.1
   B. 3.9
   C. 4.7
   D. 5.75

9. Find the upper quartile value of the data.
   {1.4, 1.3, 1.3, 9.6, 7.3, 2.3, 5.7, 9.9, 4.3,
   7.5, 3.7, 7.1, 2.7}

   A. 5.6
   B. 7.4
   C. 7.5
   D. 9.9

10. Find the maximum value of the data.
    {8.8, 4.6, 2.0, 3.4, 7.2, 2.7, 8.3, 3.0}

    A. 2.0
    B. 7.2
    C. 8.3
    D. 8.8

11. What is the lower quartile value of the data?
{4.5, 8.3, 4.0, 8.1, 3.3, 1.0, 4.5, 6.7, 1.2, 6.4}

A. 1.0

B. 3.3

C. 4.0

D. 4.5

12. Rakesh surveyed several people and found out how many hours of television they watched in a weekend. The results were 2.8, 8.4, 2.3, 4.5, 8.9, 6.2, 8.2, 1.3, 4.9, 9.4, 4.0, 9.3, 2.1, and 2.7. What is the median?

A. 1.3

B. 2.7

C. 4.5

D. 4.7

13. Find the upper quartile value of the data.
{4, 22, 22, 20, 15, 3, 16, 15, 22, 21}

A. 15

B. 16

C. 22

D. 24

14. A group of students took turns guessing a number that the teacher was thinking about. Their guesses were 10, 2, 20, 13, 3, 13, 2, 14, 2, 3, 12, and 3. What is the lower quartile value of the data?

A. 2

B. 2.5

C. 3

D. 6.5

15. What is the upper quartile value of the data?
{21, 12, 7, 12, 18, 8, 19, 25}

A. 10

B. 19.5

C. 20

D. 21

16. Fifteen students took an English exam. The upper quartile value is the median of which of the following?

A. middle 5 scores

B. greatest 5 scores

C. greatest 7 scores

D. greatest 8 scores

17. Twenty farmers compared the amount of corn they grew last year. The lower quartile value is the median of which of the following?

A. least 5 amounts

B. least 9 amounts

C. least 10 amounts

D. middle 6 amounts

18. The median of a set of 17 numbers divides the set into which of the following?

A. two sets of 8 each

B. two sets, one with 8 and the other with 9

C. two sets of 9 each

D. three sets of 6 each

19. Twenty-two different companies reported sales for the year 2001. The upper quartile value is the median of which of the following?

A. least 11 amounts

B. middle 11 amounts

C. greatest 11 amounts

D. greatest 12 amounts

20. Thirty-one contestants competed in a weight lifting competition. The lower quartile value of their scores is the median of which of the following?

A. least 10 amounts

B. least 15 amounts

C. least 16 amounts

D. middle 10 amounts

Interpreting Scatterplots

LESSON 52

You will learn how to:

- create a scatterplot
- use a scatterplot to make predictions

Key Words: scatterplot, correlation

Theo drained the pool in his backyard. He created a chart to keep track of the water level in the pool while he was draining it. He wants to use the data to create a graph that will help him predict when the pool will be empty.

Time (hours)	1	2	3	4	5	6	7	8	9	10
Water Level (feet)	10	9.25	8.5	7.75	7	6.25	5.5	4.75	4	3.25

Theo can use a scatterplot to help him predict when the water level will reach zero. A *scatterplot* is a way to represent two numerical sets of data on a graph using points. The values in one set are used as the *x*-coordinates, and the values in the other set are used as the corresponding *y*-coordinates. If time is involved, it is generally represented on the horizontal axis.

Example: Create a scatterplot using Theo's data.

Points

(1, 10)	(6, 6.25)
(2, 9.25)	(7, 5.5)
(3, 8.5)	(8, 4.75)
(4, 7.75)	(9, 4)
(5, 7)	(10, 3.25)

Use the time values for the *x*-coordinates and the water levels for the *y*-coordinates.

Graph the points with these coordinates to create your scatterplot.

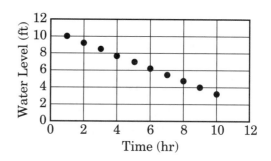

Now that you have a scatterplot of Theo's data, you can predict when the pool will be empty. To make a prediction using a scatterplot, draw a prediction line through the points on the scatterplot. A prediction line will include and be close to as many points as possible.

Example: Use the scatterplot above to predict when Theo's pool will be empty.

Draw a prediction line on the scatterplot to estimate when the water level will reach zero. The water level will probably reach zero after about 14 hours.

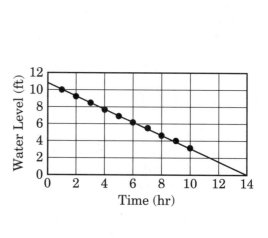

206

When you look at a scatterplot, you can sometimes see a clear pattern that may suggest a relationship between the *x* and *y* values. That relationship can be called correlation. *Correlation* is the general relationship between two sets of numerical data.

While there is a way to mathematically determine the correlation between data sets, you can also look at a scatterplot to informally describe the correlation. If the *y*-coordinates increase as the *x*-coordinates increase, the correlation is said to be positive. If the *y*-coordinates decrease as the *x*-coordinates increase, the correlation is said to be negative. The closer the points are to forming a straight line, the stronger the apparent correlation is.

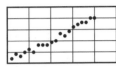   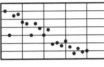 

There appears to be a strong positive correlation in the scatterplot.

There appears to be a weak positive correlation in the scatterplot.

There appears to be a strong negative correlation in the scatterplot.

There appears to be a weak negative correlation in the scatterplot.

There appears to be no correlation in the scatterplot.

Example: Informally describe the correlation between the data sets represented by the scatterplot.

In general, the *y*-coordinates are increasing as the *x*-coordinates are increasing, but the points are not close to forming a straight line. There is weak positive correlation.

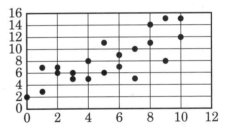

Self-Test

Circle the letter of the correct answer.

Use the scatterplot to predict the number of minutes you should expect to stay in line to get to the first position in the line.

A. 3   C. 9

B. 7   D. 16

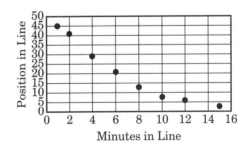

Minutes in Line

Check your answer.

D is correct.

The position and the wait are negatively correlated, and a rough estimate is that the point (16, 1) would follow the pattern of the scatterplot.

Lesson 52: Interpreting Scatterplots

Practice

Interpreting Scatterplots

Circle the letter of the correct answer.

1. What conclusion could you draw from the scatterplot?

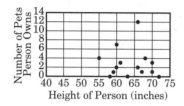

   A. Tall persons own more pets than shorter persons.

   B. More dogs are owned as pets than cats.

   C. Tall persons generally do not like animals.

   D. No conclusion can be drawn based on the scatterplot.

2. Informally describe the correlation between the data sets represented by the scatterplot.

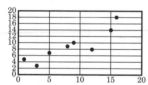

   A. strong negative

   B. weak positive

   C. strong negative

   D. no correlation

3. What conclusion could you draw from the scatterplot?

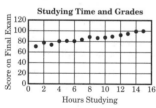

   A. No conclusion can be drawn based on the scatterplot.

   B. As study time increased, test scores decreased.

   C. Students who spent more time studying generally earned a higher grade on the final exam.

   D. A high test score does not mean you are smart.

4. What conclusion could you draw from the scatterplot?

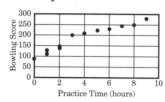

   A. The more a bowler practices, the higher the score is likely to be.

   B. Bowlers with lower scores practice often.

   C. As practice time increases, bowling scores decrease.

   D. No conclusion can be drawn based on the scatterplot.

5. Use the scatterplot to determine which of the following amounts could reasonably be the amount collected after day 15.

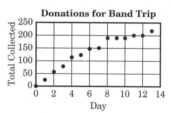

   A. $25

   B. $133

   C. $245

   D. $587

6. Informally describe the correlation between the data sets represented by the scatterplot.

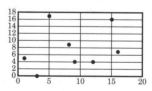

   A. strong positive

   B. weak positive

   C. strong negative

   D. no correlation

Lesson 52: Interpreting Scatterplots

7. Use the scatterplot to predict how many times a car that gets 44 mpg will stop for gas.

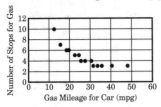

A. 3

B. 4

C. 5

D. 6

8. Use the scatterplot to determine which of the following amounts could reasonably be the annual income of someone who went to school for 23 years.

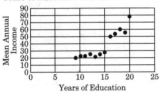

A. $40,000

B. $82,000

C. $315,000

D. $825,000

9. What conclusion could you draw from the scatterplot?

A. As golfers increased their practice times, their scores dropped.

B. Golf is a sport that does not require much practice time.

C. Golfers who spent more time practicing had higher scores.

D. No conclusion can be drawn based on the scatterplot.

10. Use the scatterplot to determine which of the following number of hours could reasonably be the length of the trip of a car with an average speed of 70 mph.

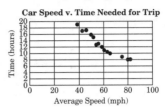

A. 9.1

B. 14

C. 17.6

D. 20

11. Informally describe the correlation between the data sets represented by the scatterplot.

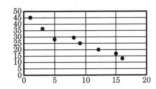

A. strong positive

B. weak positive

C. strong negative

D. no correlation

12. Use the scatterplot to determine which of the following could reasonably be the number of hours needed to read a 500 page book.

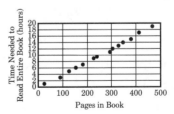

A. 5

B. 10

C. 20

D. 40

Creating and Interpreting Various Data Plots

L E S S O N   5 3

You will learn how to:
- create and interpret stem-and-leaf plots and box-and-whisker plots

Key Words: stem-and-leaf plot, box-and-whisker plot

A *stem-and-leaf plot* is a way to organize a set of data. Each number in the data set is represented by a stem and a leaf. The stem has one or more digits. It consists of all the digits of the number except the rightmost digit. The leaf is the rightmost digit.

{105, 98, 98, 111, 100, 95, 110, 100, 113, 113}

$$\underline{1\ 0}\ \underline{5}$$
The stem is 10. --- ↑ ↑ --- The leaf is 5.

$$\underline{9}\ \underline{8}$$
The stem is 9. --- ↑ ↑ --- The leaf is 8.

To create a stem-and-leaf plot, write the stems in a column in order from least to greatest. Then write the leaves, in order from least to greatest, in rows next to the appropriate stems. In the stem-and-leaf plot at the right, the element 98 is indicated by the circled digits. You can use a stem-and-leaf plot to find a mean, median, or mode.

```
 ⑨ | 5 ⑧ 8
10 | 0 0 5
11 | 0 1 3 3
     ↑         ↑
   stems    leaves
```
There is one leaf for every data item.

Example: Create a stem-and-leaf plot for the data. Then find the median.
{11.3, 11.0, 10.8, 10.9, 10.9, 11.0, 11.1, 11.2, 11.3, 12.0, 12.1}

Write the data in order from least to greatest. Identify the stems. <u>10</u>.8, <u>10</u>.9, <u>10</u>.9, <u>11</u>.0, <u>11</u>.0, <u>11</u>.1, <u>11</u>.2, <u>11</u>.3, <u>11</u>.3, <u>12</u>.0, <u>12</u>.1

The stems are 10, 11, and 12. Now identify the leaves and create the plot. Two ways of creating the stem-and-leaf plot are shown. Notice that a key, or legend, is needed if the decimal point is not included in the column of stems.

```
10. | 8 9 9
11. | 0 0 [1] 2 3 3
12. | 0 1
```

```
10 | 8 9 9
11 | 0 0 [1] 2 3 3
12 | 0 1        10|5 = 10.5
```

There are 11 data items, so the median is the 6th one. The 6th leaf and its corresponding stem are indicated in the stem-and-leaf plot. The median is 11.1.

A *box-and-whisker plot* is a display that shows how the data in a set are distributed. A box-and-whisker plot does not show every item in the data set, but it does show certain key items. It shows the minimum, the lower quartile, the median, the upper quartile, and the maximum. The minimum and maximum are represented by the ends of the whiskers and the quartiles by the ends of the box. The vertical line segment in the middle of the box represents the median.

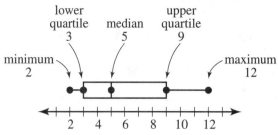

Example: Create a box-and-whisker plot for the data set.
{13, 5, 1, 15, 7, 17, 8, 15, 14, 22, 15}

Write the data items in increasing order.
Identify the minimum, median, and maximum.

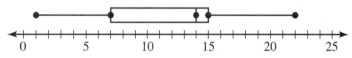

Identify the lower quartile and upper quartile.

1, 5, 7, 8, 13   15, 15, 15, 17, 22
        ↑   ↑
  lower quartile   upper quartile

Use the five numbers to create the box-and-whisker plot.

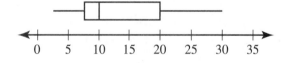

Self-Test

Circle the letter of the correct answer.

What is the upper quartile value for the data set represented by the box-and-whisker plot?

A. 5   C. 20

B. 10   D. 30

Check your answer.

C is correct.

The right end of the box represents the upper quartile. The number line indicates that the right end of the box is located at 20.

Practice

Creating and Interpreting Various Data Plots

Circle the letter of the correct answer.

1. Which number is not represented in the stem-and-leaf plot?

```
1 | 1 5 8
2 | 4 4
3 | 3 6 7 8 9 9
4 | 4 6 6 7
5 | 0
6 | 1 8
7 | 9          7|7 = 77
```

(A.) 16
B. 36
C. 50
D. 68

2. What is the minimum value of the data set represented by the stem-and-leaf plot?

```
1 | 5 5 6
2 | 0 3 4 4 7
3 | 1 2
4 | 0
5 | 9
6 | 1 1 1
7 | 8          2|8 = 2.8
```

A. 0
B. 1.5
C. 2
D. 15

3. What is the lower quartile value for the data set represented by the stem-and-leaf plot?

```
0 | 3 4 5 6
1 | 3 4 7 8
2 | 0 3     2|5 = 25
```

A. 3
B. 5
C. 13.5
D. 18

4. Create a box-and-whisker plot for the data. {20, 19, 19, 11, 35, 40, 39}

A.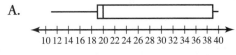
10 12 14 16 18 20 22 24 26 28 30 32 34 36 38 40

B.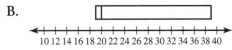
10 12 14 16 18 20 22 24 26 28 30 32 34 36 38 40

C.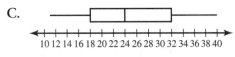
10 12 14 16 18 20 22 24 26 28 30 32 34 36 38 40

D.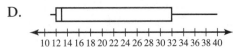
10 12 14 16 18 20 22 24 26 28 30 32 34 36 38 40

5. What is the maximum value of the data set represented by the stem-and-leaf plot?

```
 5 | 4 8 7
 6 |
 7 | 8 8 8 9
 8 | 9
 9 | 1 2 4 8 8
10 | 0          5|6 = 56
```

A. 9
B. 10
C. 98
D. 100

6. {2.5, 1.5, 6.6, 6.4, 9.1, 8.7, 2.8, 1.8, 3.8, 7.9, 8.6, 4.4, 6.9}
Which of the following could reasonably be a box-and-whisker plot for the data?

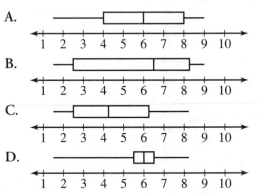

A.
1 2 3 4 5 6 7 8 9 10

B.
1 2 3 4 5 6 7 8 9 10

C.
1 2 3 4 5 6 7 8 9 10

D.
1 2 3 4 5 6 7 8 9 10

7. What is the median of the data set represented by the stem-and-leaf plot?

```
10 | 5
11 | 2
12 |
13 | 7 9
14 | 1 5
15 | 3 5 8     12|9 = 129
```

A. 139
B. 140
C. 141
D. 147

8. Which number is not represented in the stem-and-leaf plot?

```
10 | 3 4 8
11 | 5 6
12 | 0 1 2 3 4
13 |
14 | 8
15 | 7 9        12|4 = 124
```

A. 120
B. 130
C. 148
D. 157

Lesson 53: Creating and Interpreting Various Data Plots

9. It appears that 45 is the _____ of the data set represented by the box-and-whisker plot.

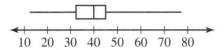

- A. minimum value
- B. median
- C. upper quartile value
- D. maximum value

10. What is the median of the data set represented by the box-and-whisker plot?

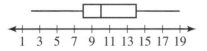

- A. 2
- B. 8
- C. 10
- D. 14

11. What is the median height represented by the stem-and-leaf plot?

Height in Inches
```
5 | 6
6 | 0 2 2 3 4 6 7 8
7 | 0 2              7|0 = 70
```

- A. 62 inches
- B. 64 inches
- C. 71.5 inches
- D. 80 inches

12. For the box-and-whisker plot, which of the following could be 131?

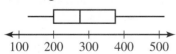

- A. minimum value
- B. lower quartile value
- C. median
- D. upper quartile value

13. What is the maximum value of the data set represented by the stem-and-leaf plot?

```
20 | 2 3 7 8
21 | 6 9
22 | 0 1 1
23 | 5 5
24 | 2              20|4 = 2.04
```

- A. 2.42
- B. 20.2
- C. 24.2
- D. 202

14. What is the median of the data set represented by the box-and-whisker plot?

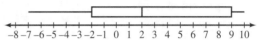

- A. −2
- B. 2
- C. 9
- D. 10

15. What is the maximum of the data?

```
1 | 0 2 2 5 7
2 | 1 3 3 3 4 8
3 | 5 6 7
4 | 8 9
5 | 3 4 4 6      7|0 = 70
```

- A. 44
- B. 50
- C. 56
- D. 65

16. What is the minimum of the data?

```
10 | 8 9 9
11 | 0 0 1 2 3 3
12 | 0 1              10|5 = 105
```

- A. 18
- B. 100
- C. 108
- D. 121

Identifying and Validating Statistical Claims

L E S S O N   5 4

You will learn how to:
• identify valid claims based on statistical data

Key Words: claim, statistics, survey, valid, bias

"More People Choose Sardine Flavored Gum!" The advertisement caught Tanya's eye. How could that be possible? It seemed unlikely that sardine was a popular flavor for gum. The statement is a *claim,* because it is presented as a fact. Was it true? Tanya reasoned that the only way to determine if it was true would be to ask everyone, and that would not be possible. She also realized that the claim was vague because of the word "more." The word "more" is used to compare quantities. The claim does not compare the number of people who choose sardine gum to any other group of people.

Statistics deals with collecting, organizing, and analyzing data. Data is often collected by means of a *survey,* in which a group of people is asked one or more questions.

The truth of a claim is often difficult to establish, so statisticians attempt to determine if a claim is valid instead. A claim is considered *valid* if it is logically based on the data.

In order to get even closer to the truth, it is desirable that bias is avoided in collecting the data. *Bias* is a tendency to influence the data. Bias will be present in a survey if there is any reason that a participant may not give an honest answer. The survey group may be biased if it lacks variety.

Example: The employees of Ace Candy Co. were asked by their boss to name their favorite candy. The result was that 85% of the employees named Ace as their favorite candy. The company advertised that 85% of those surveyed preferred Ace candy. What are some possible sources of bias in the survey?

The survey only included company employees. Because of their personal interest in this company, the results of the survey are biased. Another possible source of bias is the person conducting the survey. Some employees may not have been willing to tell their boss that they liked another company's candy better.

If a conclusion or claim is based on a graph, examine the graph carefully.

Example: Mary looked at the graph and concluded that the average price of popcorn has more than doubled in the last ten years. Is this a valid claim, based on the graph?

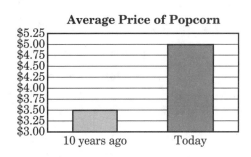

Average Price of Popcorn

The second bar is at least twice as high as the first. However, the vertical scale does not begin at zero. The price has increased from $3.50 to $5.00 in the last ten years. The average price has not doubled, so the claim is not valid.

Be careful to base conclusions only on the information provided.

Example: At the right are the results of a school survey question "Which do you prefer, chocolate or vanilla?"

	males	females
chocolate	88%	66%
vanilla	12%	34%

Mel said that, based on the survey, more males than females preferred chocolate. Was Mel's claim valid?

No, his claim was not valid. The number of males and females are not in the survey results, so his claim is not logically based on the data.

Self-Test

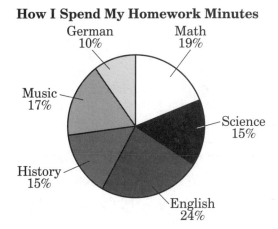

How I Spend My Homework Minutes

Circle the letter of the correct answer.

Which of the following is a valid claim based on the information given in the graph?

A. The student studied for 100 minutes.
B. The student devoted the most time to English.
C. English is the student's hardest subject.
D. German is easy.

Check your answer.

B is correct.

The only claim that is logically based on the graph is "The student devoted the most time to English." Claims C and D are not logically based on the data because time spent on homework does not necessarily indicate the difficulty of the homework. And while the percents do total 100, the actual number of minutes studied is not given in the graph.

Practice

Identifying and Validating Statistical Claims

Circle the letter of the correct answer.

1. Which of the following is a valid claim based on the information given in the graph?

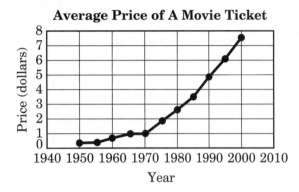

Average Price of A Movie Ticket

A. The average price of a movie ticket will always increase from year to year.

B. The price of movie tickets is too high.

C. From 1950 to 2000 the average price of a movie ticket has more than doubled.

D. More people went to the movies in 2000 than in 1960.

2. Suppose you want to conduct a survey to determine which band the student body would like to play at a school dance. Which of the following would help to guard against bias in your survey?

A. Call your 5 best friends and ask only their opinions.

B. Survey the parents in your neighborhood.

C. Ask every 5th person who enters the cafeteria for lunch for their opinion.

D. Ask the first 2 people you see at school one day.

3. Which of the following is a valid claim based on the information given in the graph?

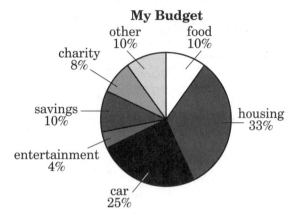

My Budget

A. Housing is more expensive now than in 1971.

B. This person is very generous.

C. You should save 10% of your money every month.

D. This person spends more on her car than on entertainment.

4. Which of the following is a valid claim based on the information given in the graph?

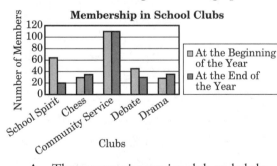

Membership in School Clubs

A. The community service club ended the year with the same number of members as it started with.

B. The school does not have much school spirit.

C. Most students do not like chess.

D. The debate club has the fewest members.

5. Which of the following is a valid claim based on the information given in the graph?

Results of 100 Rolls of a Die

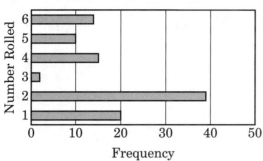

A. The number 1 was rolled twice as many times as the number 5.

B. The number 3 was rolled half as many times as the number 5.

C. The die was not a fair die.

D. Odd numbers are easier to roll than even numbers.

6. A survey will be conducted to try to determine the most popular fruit in the United States. Which survey group is the least likely to produce bias?

A. a randomly selected group of supermarket customers

B. a group of apple farmers

C. the employees of a major orange juice manufacturer

D. the owners of peach farms in Georgia

7. Which of the following is a valid claim based on the information given in the graph?

School Attendance

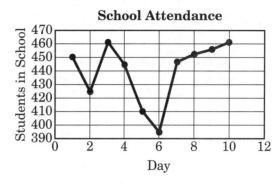

A. There are about 460 students enrolled in the school.

B. Many students went on a field trip on day 6.

C. The greatest drop in attendance was from day 4 to day 5.

D. No student at this school has perfect attendance.

8. Which of the following is a valid claim based on the information given in the graph?

Number of Straight A Students

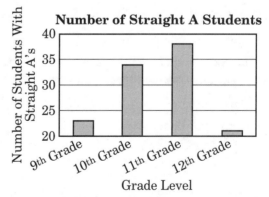

A. There were three times as many straight A students in 10th grade as in 9th grade.

B. 12th graders are lazy.

C. There were about 4 more straight A students in 11th grade as in 10th grade.

D. 9th graders work harder than 12th graders.

Calculating the Probability of an Event and Its Complement

LESSON 55

You will learn how to:

• calculate the probability of an event and its complement

• express the probability of an event as a ratio, percent, or decimal

Key Words: event, probability, complement

Erik is playing a game at a carnival. He reaches his hand into a box that contains 10 ping-pong balls, numbered 1 through 10. If he picks the 7, he wins a ticket for a free ride. What is the probability that he will pick the 7?

There are 10 possible outcomes: 1, 2, 3, 4, 5, 6, 7, 8, 9, and 10. There is 1 chance in 10 that he will pick a 7, so the probability that he picks a 7 is $\frac{1}{10}$.

An *event* is an outcome or group of outcomes. When all possible outcomes are equally likely, the *probability* of an event, written $P(E)$, is given by the formula $P(E) = \frac{\text{Number of Favorable Outcomes}}{\text{Number of Possible Outcomes}}$.

The probability of Erik picking the 7 is written as $P(7) = \frac{1}{10}$. You can think of a favorable outcome as any way in which the event occurs.

Probability can also be expressed as a percent or a decimal.

Example: Write the probability of Erik picking the 7 as a decimal and as a percent.

$P(7) = \frac{1}{10} = 0.1$ $P(7) = \frac{1}{10} = \frac{10}{100} = 10\%$

A probability is always at least zero and less than or equal to one. For example, the probability that Erik will pick the number 12 is zero, because there is no ball numbered with a 12.

The closer the probability of an event is to 1, the more likely it is to happen. The closer the probability of an event is to 0, the less likely it is to happen.

Example: $P(A) = 50\%$; $P(B) = \frac{1}{3}$; $P(C) = 0.79$. Write the events A, B, and C in order from least likely to occur to most likely to occur.

Write each probability as a decimal and compare them.

$P(A) = 50\% = 0.50$ $P(B) = \frac{1}{3} \approx 0.33$ $P(C) = 0.79$

$0.33 < 0.50 < 0.79$ $P(B) < P(A) < P(C)$

The events in order from least likely to occur to most likely to occur are *B, A,* and *C*.

Example: The letters of the word MATH are individually written on four cards. One lettered card is chosen at random. Find the probability of choosing a consonant.

There are 3 favorable outcomes (M, T, and H) and 4 possible outcomes (M, A, T, and H).

$$P(\text{consonant}) = \frac{\text{Number of consonants}}{\text{Total number of letters}} = \frac{3}{4}$$

The *complement* of an event consists of all the outcomes that are not part of the event. Find the probability of not choosing a consonant. The only letter that is not a consonant is A.

$$P(\text{choosing other than a consonant}) = \frac{\text{number of letters that are not consonants}}{\text{total number of letters}} = \frac{1}{4}$$

The events "choosing a consonant" and "choosing other than a consonant" are complements of each other. Notice that $1 - \frac{3}{4} = \frac{1}{4}$, and $1 - \frac{1}{4} = \frac{3}{4}$.

For any event A, *P(the complement of A) = 1 - P(A).*

To find the probability of the complement of an event, you can subtract the probability of the event from 1.

Example: Colin guessed the answers to 3 multiple choice questions on a test. The probability that he guessed the correct answer on all 3 questions is $\frac{1}{12}$. What is the probability that he did **not** answer all 3 questions correctly?

$P(\text{not answering all 3 questions correctly}) = 1 - P(\text{answering all 3 questions correctly})$

$P(\text{not answering all 3 questions correctly}) = 1 - \frac{1}{12} = \frac{11}{12}$

Self-Test

Circle the letter of the correct answer.

Mr. Paul has 25 students in his class. Twelve of those students are boys and thirteen are girls. Mr. Paul will randomly choose one student in his class to receive a new calculator. What is the probability he will choose a girl?

A. 13%
B. 48%
C. 50%
D. 52%

Check your answer.

D is correct.

$$P(girl) = \frac{\text{Number of girls}}{\text{Number of students}} = \frac{13}{25} = \frac{52}{100} = 52\%$$

Practice

Calculating the Probability of an Event and Its Complement

Circle the letter of the correct answer.

1. $P(A) = 0.25$; $P(B) = 0.6$; $P(C) = 80\%$; $P(D) = 9\%$. Which event is the least likely to occur?

   A. A

   B. B

   C. C

   D. D

2. The faces of a cube are numbered from 1 to 6. What is the probability of rolling a 5?

   A. 0

   B. $\frac{1}{6}$

   C. $\frac{1}{5}$

   D. $\frac{5}{6}$

3. $P(A) = \frac{9}{11}$. What is the probability that event A will not occur?

   A. $\frac{1}{11}$

   B. $\frac{2}{11}$

   C. $\frac{9}{11}$

   D. $\frac{10}{11}$

4. A bag contains 2 white marbles, 1 red marble, 1 green marble, and 1 purple marble. What is the probability of reaching in the bag and randomly choosing a white marble?

   A. 0.02

   B. 0.2

   C. 0.25

   D. 0.4

5. $P(A) = \frac{2}{3}$; $P(B) = \frac{5}{12}$; $P(C) = 50\%$. Put the events A, B, and C in order from least likely to occur to most likely to occur.

   A. A, B, C

   B. C, B, A

   C. A, C, B

   D. B, C, A

6. The probability that a randomly selected candy in a bag will be chocolate is 0.7. What is the probability that a randomly selected candy will not be chocolate?

   A. 0.03

   B. 0.07

   C. 0.3

   D. 0.7

7. $P(A) = \frac{3}{4}$; $P(B) = 0.9$; $P(C) = 77\%$; $P(D) = \frac{4}{5}$. Which event is the most likely to occur?

   A. A

   B. B

   C. C

   D. D

8. The letters of the word MATH are written individually on four cards. One lettered card is chosen at random. Find the probability of choosing a vowel.

   A. 25%

   B. $\frac{1}{3}$

   C. 0.4

   D. 1

Lesson 55: Calculating the Probability of an Event and Its Complement

9. A fair spinner is numbered from 1 to 10, with each number equally likely. What is the probability of getting an even number on a spin?

   A. 0
   B. 50%
   C. $\frac{7}{10}$
   D. 1

10. Victor has eight names in his address book: Allie, Brenda, Carla, Devon, Edgar, Fuschia, Gordon, and Heidi. If he chooses one name at random, what is the probability that the name he chooses ends with a vowel?

   A. 0.25
   B. 0.375
   C. 0.5
   D. 0.625

11. A fair spinner has ten areas, labeled A to J, with all areas equally likely. What is the probability of spinning and getting a letter that appears in the word HAPPY?

   A. 20%
   B. 30%
   C. 40%
   D. 50%

12. $P(A) = \frac{7}{10}$; $P(B) = \frac{2}{7}$; $P(C) = \frac{5}{6}$. Put the events A, B, and C in order from least likely to occur to most likely to occur.

   A. A, C, B
   B. C, B, A
   C. B, C, A
   D. B, A, C

13. The probability that a randomly selected class member is male is $\frac{1}{7}$. What is the probability that a randomly selected class member is female?

   A. $\frac{1}{7}$
   B. $\frac{1}{6}$
   C. $\frac{6}{7}$
   D. 6

14. A fair spinner is numbered from 1 to 10, with each number equally likely. What is the probability of getting a number less than 6 on a spin?

   A. 0.2
   B. 0.5
   C. 0.75
   D. 0.8

15. A standard deck of playing cards has 52 cards. The cards are divided into 4 suits: hearts, clubs, spades, and diamonds. There are 13 cards in each suit. What is the probability of selecting a diamond from the deck?

   A. $\frac{1}{13}$
   B. $\frac{1}{4}$
   C. $\frac{4}{13}$
   D. $\frac{31}{52}$

16. A standard deck of playing cards has 52 cards. The cards are divided equally into 4 suits: hearts, clubs, spades, and diamonds. There are 13 cards in each suit: 2, 3, 4, 5, 6, 7, 8, 9, 10, Jack, Queen, King, and Ace. What is the probability of selecting a 10 of clubs from the deck?

   A. $\frac{1}{52}$
   B. $\frac{1}{13}$
   C. 25%
   D. 0.52

Identifying and Calculating the Probability of Compound Events

LESSON 56

> You will learn how to:
> - make a tree diagram to show all possible outcomes of an experiment
> - find the probability of a compound event
> - distinguish between independent and dependent events
>
> **Key Words:** tree diagram, sample space, compound event, independent events, dependent events

Alex wants to conduct a probability experiment. The experiment is to spin the spinner and flip the coin.

Example: List all the possible outcomes for Alex's experiment.

Use the *tree diagram* at the right. The set of all the possible outcomes is called the *sample space*.

The sample space for this experiment is {(1, H), (1, T), (2, H), (2, T), (3, H), (3, T), (4, H), (4, T)}. The branch on the diagram from 3 to T represents the outcome (3, T).

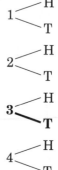

Example: What is the probability of Alex spinning an even number and getting a head on the flip?

The probability of an event E is given by the formula $P(E) = \dfrac{\text{Number of Favorable Outcomes}}{\text{Number of Possible Outcomes}}$.

There are 8 possible outcomes, 2 of which are favorable: (2, H) and (4, H).

The probability of Alex spinning an even number and getting a head on the flip is

$P(\text{even and head}) = \frac{2}{8} = \frac{1}{4}$.

The event "spinning an even number and getting a head on the flip" consists of more than one outcome, so it is called a *compound event*. It can be written as a subset of the sample space: {(2, H), (4, H)}.

There is another way to find the same probability. Consider the spin and the flip to be two separate experiments. Then "spinning an even number" and "getting a head" are two separate events. To find the probability of a compound event, you can multiply the probabilities of the events that form the compound event.

$P(\text{even and head}) = P(\text{even}) \cdot P(\text{head}) = \frac{2}{4} \cdot \frac{1}{2} = \frac{1}{2} \cdot \frac{1}{2} = \frac{1}{4}$

To be sure that you are multiplying the correct probabilities, it is necessary to determine whether the events are dependent or independent. If the occurrence of one event has no effect on the probability of the other, then the events are *independent events*. If the occurrence of one event affects the probability of the other, then the events are *dependent events*.

Suppose there is a bag containing 4 red marbles and 3 yellow marbles. You want to find the probability of picking a yellow marble and then a red marble. If the marble is replaced after the first pick, the events are independent. If the marble is not replaced, the events are dependent.

Example: A bag contains 4 red marbles and 3 yellow marbles. What is the probability of selecting a yellow marble and then selecting a red marble?

	With replacement (independent events)	Without replacement (dependent events)
1st pick	$P(Y) = \frac{3}{7}$	$P(Y) = \frac{3}{7}$
2nd pick	$P(R) = \frac{4}{7}$	$P(R) = \frac{4}{6}$ (6 marbles remain after the 1st pick)
	$P(Y, \text{then } R) = \frac{3}{7} \cdot \frac{4}{7} = \frac{12}{49} \approx 24\%$	$P(Y, \text{then } R) = \frac{3}{7} \cdot \frac{4}{6} = \frac{12}{42} \approx 29\%$

Self-Test

Circle the letter of the correct answer.

A bag contains 4 red marbles and 3 yellow marbles. What is the probability of selecting a yellow marble and then selecting another yellow marble from the remaining marbles?

A. 12%

B. 14%

C. 18%

D. 21%

Check your answer.

B is correct.

1st *pick:* $P(Y) = \frac{3}{7}$

2nd *pick:* $P(Y) = \frac{2}{6}$ *because 2 of the remaining 6 marbles are yellow.*

$\frac{3}{7} \cdot \frac{2}{6} = \frac{6}{42} \approx 14\%$.

Practice

Identifying and Calculating the Probability of Compound Events

Circle the letter of the correct answer.

1. A numbered cube with numbers 1 through 6 is rolled twice. What is the probability that the same number is rolled twice?

   A. $\frac{1}{36}$

   B. $\frac{1}{20}$

   C. $\frac{1}{12}$

   D. $\frac{1}{6}$

2. A numbered cube with numbers 1 through 6 is rolled twice. What is the probability that the sum of the two rolls will be 4?

   A. $\frac{1}{36}$

   B. $\frac{1}{12}$

   C. $\frac{1}{9}$

   D. $\frac{1}{4}$

3. Lou has a coin and a cube numbered 1 through 6. What is the probability of tossing the coin and getting tails and then rolling an even number on the cube?

   A. $\frac{1}{4}$

   B. $\frac{1}{2}$

   C. $\frac{2}{3}$

   D. 1

4. A bag contains 3 chocolate candies, 5 strawberry candies, and 2 mint candies. What is the probability of randomly selecting a chocolate candy, and then reaching in the bag and selecting another chocolate candy from the pieces remaining in the bag?

   A. $\frac{1}{20}$

   B. $\frac{1}{15}$

   C. $\frac{9}{100}$

   D. $\frac{1}{10}$

5. If a coin is flipped twice, what is the probability of getting a tail followed by a head?

   A. 25%

   B. 50%

   C. 75%

   D. 100%

6. What is the probability of picking a red card from a standard deck of 52 cards, putting it back, and then drawing a red card again?

   A. $\frac{1}{16}$

   B. $\frac{1}{8}$

   C. $\frac{1}{4}$

   D. $\frac{1}{2}$

7. A bag contains 10 marbles numbered 1 through 10. What is the probability that a 5 is drawn at random, is replaced, and then an even numbered marble is drawn?

   A. 5%

   B. 10%

   C. 25%

   D. 50%

8. A bag contains 9 marbles numbered 1 through 9. What is the probability that a 5 is drawn at random, and then an even numbered marble is drawn from the remaining marbles?

   A. $\frac{1}{45}$

   B. $\frac{4}{81}$

   C. $\frac{1}{18}$

   D. $\frac{1}{9}$

9. Choose the events that are NOT independent.

   A. Flipping a coin twice and getting heads two times.

   B. Selecting a red marble from a bag then selecting a blue marble from the remaining marbles in the bag.

   C. Rolling a die three times and getting an odd number each time.

   D. Selecting a red marble from a bag, putting it back in, then selecting a blue marble from the bag.

10. A letter is chosen randomly from the word CHAIR. What is the sample space of the event?

   A. {C, H, R}

   B. {C, H, A, I, R}

   C. {A, I}

   D. {C, H, I, R}

11. A blue plate special at Alice's Restaurant consists of 1 meat and 2 different vegetables. You can choose from four different meats and six different vegetables. How many possible blue-plate specials exist?

   A. 10

   B. 24

   C. 120

   D. 576

12. What is the probability of tossing a coin and getting heads, then tossing the same coin and getting tails?

   A. 0%

   B. 15%

   C. 25%

   D. 50%

13. The letters from the word MATH are written individually on 4 cards and placed face down on a table. What is the probability of randomly selecting the "M," and then randomly selecting the "H" from the remaining cards?

   A. $\frac{1}{16}$

   B. $\frac{1}{12}$

   C. $\frac{1}{8}$

   D. $\frac{7}{12}$

14. John is selecting stationary at the post office. There are nine different page styles and three different envelope styles. How many combinations are there?

   A. 9

   B. 12

   C. 20

   D. 27

15. A numbered cube with numbers 1 through 6 is rolled and a coin is tossed. Which outcome is NOT in the sample space of the event?

   A. 6 and heads

   B. 3 and tails

   C. 0 and tails

   D. 4 and heads

16. What is the probability of tossing a coin twice and getting heads both times?

   A. $\frac{1}{4}$

   B. $\frac{1}{3}$

   C. $\frac{1}{2}$

   D. $\frac{3}{4}$

Solving Word Problems

LESSON 57

You will learn how to:
• apply various techniques to solve word problems

Key Words: generalize, irrelevant

You will often need to <u>identify a relationship</u> to solve a word problem.

Example: Joe drove for 2 hours at an average speed of 55 miles per hour (mph) and for 3 hours at an average speed of 60 mph. Find the average speed for the entire trip.

To solve this problem, you need to know the relationship *(rate)(time) = distance.* To find the average speed for the entire trip, divide the total number of miles by the total time.

2 hours at 55 mph = 110 miles	miles driven at average speed of 55 mph
3 hours at 60 mph = 180 miles	miles driven at average speed of 60 mph
110 miles + 180 miles = 290 miles	total miles for the entire trip
2 hours + 3 hours = 5 hours	total time for the entire trip
290 ÷ 5 = 58 mph	average speed for the entire trip
The average speed for the entire trip was 58 mph.	

Sometimes you will need to <u>identify a pattern</u>.

Example: What is the 8th number in the sequence 3, 7, 11, 15, … ?

Each number is 4 more than the previous number in the sequence.

1st	2nd	3rd	4th	5th	6th	7th	8th
3	7	11	15	19	23	27	31

You may need to <u>generalize information from a simpler problem</u> to solve another problem. To ***generalize*** means to decide how to apply what you have learned to other cases.

Example: What is the 1,000th number in the sequence 3, 7, 11, 15, … ?

It is not practical to write 1,000 numbers. You need to find an expression that you can use to find any number in the sequence.

1st	2nd	3rd	--------	n^{th}
3	7	11	--------	
$4 \cdot 1 - 1$	$4 \cdot 2 - 1$	$4 \cdot 3 - 1$	--------	$4n - 1$

The 1,000th number in the sequence is $4 \cdot 1{,}000 - 1 = 4{,}000 - 1 = 3{,}999$.

A word problem may contain more information than needed. This extra information is *irrelevant;* it should be disregarded.

Example: Identify the irrelevant information.

Carson is a DJ at a local radio station. He works 30 hours each week and answers about 100 phone calls each day. He earns $15 per hour. How much does Carson earn in one week?
The irrelevant information is that Carson is a DJ and answers about 100 phone calls each day. To solve the problem, multiply the number of hours he works each week by his hourly pay:
30 hours per week · $15 per hour = $450 per week.

If certain information is missing from a word problem, it may not be possible to solve it.

Example: What additional information is needed to solve the problem?

What is the volume of a rectangular prism 2 ft long and 4 ft wide?
The missing information is the third dimension of the prism.

It may be useful to decide which piece of information to use first.

Example: There is a number that is a multiple of 4. The sum of its digits is 11, and it is between 230 and 240. What is the number?

You could start by listing all multiples of 4: 4, 8, 12, 16, …
However, it would be much faster to begin with numbers between 230 and 240. There are two that are multiples of 4: 232 and 236. The correct answer is 236, because 2 + 3 + 6 = 11.

Self-Test

Circle the letter of the correct answer.

Joe is thinking of a number less than 75. It is a multiple of 3 and 8. The sum of its digits is 12. What is the number?

A. 15   C. 32
B. 24   D. 48

Check your answer.

D is correct.

List the multiples of 8 in increasing order. The first one that is also a multiple of 3 and whose digits add up to 12 is the answer. 8, 16, 24, 32, 40, 48

Practice

Solving Word Problems

Circle the letter of the correct answer.

1. What is the 500th number in the sequence 5, 8, 11, 14, … ?

   A. 502
   B. 505
   C. 1,502
   D. 1,505

2. A number is squared and the result is the opposite of the original number. What is the original number?

   A. −2
   B. −1
   C. 0
   D. 1

3. A winning lottery number is made up of 4 odd digits. The second digit is 8 less than the third. The sum of the first and last digits is 16. The winning number is less than 8,000. What is the number?

   A. 1979
   B. 7199
   C. 7919
   D. 9197

4. A car travels at 56 mph for one hour and then travels 65 mph for two hours. What is the car's average speed over the entire trip?

   A. 58 miles per hour
   B. 60 miles per hour
   C. 61 miles per hour
   D. 62 miles per hour

5. A train travels from city A to city B at a rate of 88 miles per hour without stopping. How long did the trip take?
   What additional information is needed to solve the problem?

   A. the number of minutes in an hour
   B. the price of a ticket on the train
   C. the distance from A to B
   D. the number of stops the train makes

6. Francis used 126 feet of fencing to enclose a rectangular pen on her farm. The length of the pen was twice the width. What was the length of the pen?

   A. 21
   B. 42
   C. 63
   D. 84

7. What information is irrelevant in the following word problem?
   Wally ordered donuts—6 plain, 3 glazed, and 3 sugar. Plain donuts are $0.35 each and all other donuts are $0.40 each. What is the probability that Wally will randomly select a plain donut from his order?

   A. the price of the donuts
   B. the number of plain donuts
   C. the number of glazed donuts
   D. the number of sugar donuts

8. Find a number less than 50 that is a multiple of 2, 3, and 7.

   A. 6
   B. 21
   C. 42
   D. 84

Lesson 57: Solving Word Problems

9. If you multiply a number by 4, add 8, divide by 2 and subtract 5, the result is 3. What is the number?

A. 2
B. 3
C. 4
D. 8

10. The enrollment fees and monthly dues for four gyms are given below. You plan to join a gym for six months and spend as little money as possible. Which gym should you choose?

Gym	Enrollment Fee	Monthly Fee
A	$100	$50
B	$550	$150
C	$75	$75
D	$65	$60

A. A
B. B
C. C
D. D

11. The mean test score on a chemistry test was 89. The highest score was 97 and the lowest score was 50. How many students took the test? What additional information is needed to solve the problem?

A. the median test score
B. the sum of the test scores
C. the upper quartile value of the test scores
D. the lower quartile value of the test scores

12. What information is irrelevant in the following word problem?
The price of a radio has dropped from $25 to $20 over a 4 month period. What is the percent decrease?

A. the number of months
B. the price before the drop
C. the price after the drop
D. all of the information is relevant

13. Mr. West, Ms. East, Mr. North and Ms. South are a doctor, police officer, pharmacist, and lawyer, but not necessarily in that order. The police officer is a female. The doctor sends his patients to Mr. North for medicine. Ms. East is the lawyer. What is Ms. South's occupation?

A. doctor
B. police officer
C. pharmacist
D. lawyer

14. What additional information is needed to solve the problem?
What is the area of trapezoid with a height of 9 feet and a base length of 12 feet?

A. a picture of the trapezoid
B. the number of inches in a foot
C. the length of the other base
D. All the necessary information is given.

15. On day one, a worker is paid 1 bean. On day two the worker is paid 4 beans. The worker is paid 9 beans on the third day and 16 beans on the fourth day. How many beans will the worker receive on the sixth day if the pattern continues?

A. 12
B. 25
C. 36
D. 40

16. The fabric for Alan's costume is $2.25 per square foot. How much will he pay for 1 square yard?

A. $2.25
B. $6.75
C. $13.50
D. $20.25

Estimating Answers and Determining the Reasonableness of Answers

LESSON 58

You will learn how to:
- estimate answers
- determine the reasonableness of an answer

Peyton has completed his mathematics homework, and he wants a way to check his work for mistakes. Incorrect choice of operations, misplaced decimal points, and incorrect formulas are some common sources of mistakes.

Estimation is a good way to determine if a calculated answer is reasonable. It is also useful when you only need an approximate answer.

To estimate, choose numbers that are close in value to those in your problem but that are easier to work with. Perform the calculations with those numbers. If you only need an approximate answer, then the result is your answer. To check an answer that you have already calculated, see if the approximate answer is close to your calculated answer.

Example: $1\frac{7}{8}$ cups of water are poured into a container that already holds $2\frac{3}{4}$ cups of water. Estimate the total number of cups of water in the container.

Round each mixed number to the nearest whole number.

$1\frac{7}{8}$ rounds to 2. $2\frac{3}{4}$ rounds to 3.

$2 + 3 = 5$

The total amount of water is about 5 cups.

Example: The radius of a circle is 5 cm. Greta calculated the circumference to be approximately 314 centimeters. Use estimation to determine if Greta's answer is reasonable.

$C = 2\pi r$ ←   The formula for circumference is $C = 2\pi r$.

$C \approx 2(3)(5)$ ←   For estimating, use $\pi \approx 3$.

$C \approx 30$ Greta's calculated answer, 314 cm, is not reasonable. If Greta checks her work, she will find that she misplaced the decimal point. The correct calculated answer is 31.4 cm.

Another way to check the reasonableness of an answer is to determine if it makes sense.

Example: Lance converted 90 feet to yards and got an answer of 270. Is this answer reasonable?

No, it is not reasonable. A yard is longer than a foot, so the answer must be less than 90.

Example: Kate used the system of equations at the right to solve a problem about tickets to a play. She let $x = $ the number of adult tickets and $y = $ the number of children's tickets. She found the solution to be $x = 15$ and $y = -2$. Is her answer reasonable?

$$x + y = 13$$
$$5x + 3y = 69$$

No, it is not reasonable. It is not possible to have -2 tickets. She probably set up the system incorrectly.

Example: Estimate the area of the figure.

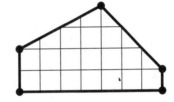

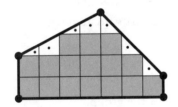

Count all the complete squares and add about half the number of partial squares. There are 16 complete squares and 7 partial squares. Use either 3 or 4 to approximate half of 7. $16 + 3 = 19$, and $16 + 4 = 20$, so either 19 square units or 20 square units is a good estimate.

Self-Test

Circle the letter of the correct answer.

Jamaal has $800 to spend on a business trip. His airfare will be $275. The hotel will cost $100 per night and food will be about $25 per day. About how many days can he plan for the trip?

A. 4   C. 10

B. 8   D. 11

Check your answer.

A is correct.
He will spend about $125 per day in addition to the $275 airfare.
$4(125) + 275 \approx 800.$

Practice

Estimating Answers and Determining the Reasonableness of Answers

Circle the letter of the correct answer.

1. Estimate the area of a square whose side has length 8.98 units.

   A. 8 square units

   B. 9 square units

   C. 64 square units

   D. 81 square units

2. Tom is twice as tall as his younger brother, Bill. Find Bill's height.
   Which of the following solutions is not reasonable based on the situation?

   A. 30 inches

   B. 35 inches

   C. 40 inches

   D. 50 inches

3. Li bought $5\frac{5}{6}$ pounds of red beans, $4\frac{2}{3}$ pounds of kidney beans, and $\frac{3}{4}$ pounds of white beans for her chili. How can Li estimate the total number of pounds of beans she purchased?

   A. $5 + 4 + 0 = 9$

   B. $6 + 5 + 1 = 12$

   C. $5 + 4 + 1 = 10$

   D. $6 + 4 + 0 = 10$

4. Estimate the area of the figure.

   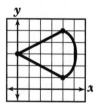

   A.   6 square units

   B. 10 square units

   C. 13 square units

   D. 16 square units

5. A circle with radius 3 inches is cut from a square piece of paper that is 25 inches on each side. The area of the remaining paper is calculated as 606.16 square inches. Which estimate could be used to check the answer?

   A. $25^2 - 3 \cdot 3^2$

   B. $25^2 - 3 \cdot 3 \cdot 2$

   C. $25^2 + 3 \cdot 3^2$

   D. $25^2 + 3 \cdot 3 \cdot 2$

6. Estimate the radius of a circle whose circumference is 31.4.

   A.   2.5

   B.   5

   C. 10

   D. 20

7. The results of a survey on the amount people spent on their last haircut are given below.
   $10.25, $25.25, $20.50, $30.50, $16.00, $19.99
   Estimate the mean of the group.

   A. $15

   B. $20

   C. $25

   D. $30

8. Estimate the area of the figure.

   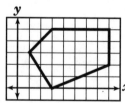

   A. 15 square units

   B. 20 square units

   C. 25 square units

   D. 30 square units

9. Which is the best method to estimate the product of $2\frac{19}{20}$, $4\frac{19}{20}$, and $2\frac{1}{32}$?

A. $3 \cdot 4 \cdot 2 = 24$

B $3 \cdot 5 \cdot 2 = 30$

C. $4 \cdot 5 \cdot 2 = 40$

D. $4 \cdot 5 \cdot 3 = 60$

10. Which is the best estimate for the number of inches in 20 yards?

A. 240

B. 360

C. 700

D. 1,000

11. George used the following system of equations to determine the weights of two boxes.

$x + y = 20$ $\quad$ x = weight of box 1

$2x - y = 70$ $\quad$ y = weight of box 2

George determined the solution to be $x = 30$ and $y = -10$. Is his answer reasonable?

A. yes, because the sum of the weights is 45

B. no, because a weight cannot be negative

C. no, the solution does not satisfy the second equation

D. no, because the weights are not equal

12. A stereo was originally priced at $202. The sale price is $160. How could you estimate the percent decrease in price?

A. $200 - 160$

B. $\frac{200 - 160}{100}$

C. $\frac{200 - 160}{200}$

D. $\frac{200 + 160}{200 + 100}$

13. Rachel has $405 to spend on food for the month of February. She spends about $75 each week on groceries and about $12 every time she eats at a restaurant. Estimate the greatest number of times she can eat at a restaurant in February.

A. 6

B. 8

C. 11

D. 15

14. Which is the best estimate for the number of heads you would expect if a coin is flipped 294 times?

A. 150

B. 190

C. 200

D. 230

15. Sales tax in Nigel's hometown is 9%. How could Nigel estimate the sales tax on an item that costs $48.97?

A. multiply 50 by 10

B. multiply 50 by 0.10

C. subtract 0.10 from 50

D. divide 50 by 0.10

16. The bar graph shows the number of pets in stock at four pet stores. About how many pets are there altogether in all four stores?

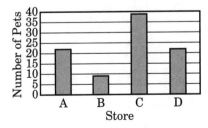

A. 70 pets

B. 80 pets

C. 90 pets

D. 100 pets

Formulating Mathematical Conjectures

LESSON 59

You will learn how to:

- formulate a mathematical conjecture
- give an example that helps to justify a conjecture
- give a counterexample to show that a conjecture is false

Key Words: mathematical conjecture, counterexample

Vince observed something about numbers that are divisible by 4. For every example he studied, the number formed by the last two digits was divisible by 4.

124   352   516   1,560   47,988 ← All of these numbers are divisible by 4.

<u>124</u>   3<u>52</u>   5<u>16</u>   1,5<u>60</u>   47,9<u>88</u> ← All of these 2-digit numbers are divisible by 4.

When Vince made his observation, he guessed that it would be true of any number that is divisible by 4. He formulated a mathematical conjecture. A *mathematical conjecture* is a statement that has not been proven true or false. A conjecture is usually based on observation of a pattern or evidence. Although he was not able to prove his conjecture, his examples helped to justify it.

Example: Give an example that helps to justify the following conjecture:
The square of an odd number is an odd number.

There are many examples that could be used; $3^2 = 9$, $9^2 = 81$, and $13^2 = 169$ are a few.

Example: Formulate a mathematical conjecture based on the following:
$2^2 = 4, 4^2 = 16, 6^2 = 36, 8^2 = 64, (-2)^2 = 4$

All the numbers that are squared are even. All the results are even. Conjecture: The square of an even number is even.

Example: Formulate a mathematical conjecture based on the following:
$\left(\frac{1}{3}\right)^2 = \frac{1}{9}, \left(\frac{2}{5}\right)^2 = \frac{4}{25}, \left(\frac{9}{10}\right)^2 = \frac{81}{100}$

Each number that is squared is between 0 and 1, and each square is less than the number itself. Conjecture: The square of a number between 0 and 1 is less than the number.

Paul made the following list of prime numbers: 5, 7, 11, 23, 37, 53.
He formulated the conjecture that all prime numbers are odd.
This conjecture is actually false. It can be proved false by
a counterexample. A **counterexample** is any example that proves
a conjecture false. Only one counterexample is necessary to prove
a statement false.

Example: Give a counterexample to show that the
conjecture "All prime numbers are odd" is false.

Counterexample: The number 2 is prime and not odd.

In this lesson, you will either give a counterexample to prove a
conjecture false, or give examples that help to justify a conjecture
that appears to be true. To prove that a conjecture is true, you must
use accepted rules of logic and a form of reasoning called deductive
reasoning. Deductive reasoning is discussed in the next lesson.

Example: Give a counterexample to show that the
following conjecture is false.
No number is a square root of itself.

Counterexample: The square root of 1 is 1.

Example: Give a counterexample to show that the
following conjecture is false:
If a polygon has all sides equal and all angles
equal, then the polygon is a square.

Counterexample: The triangle at the right.

Self-Test

Circle the letter of the correct answer.

Which of the following helps to justify the conjecture that
the sum of an odd number and an even number is odd?

A. 3 + 5 = 8   C. 2 + 4 = 6

B. 3 + 4 = 7   D. 2 · 4 = 8

Check your answer.

B is correct.

3 is odd, 4 is even, and 7 is odd.

Practice

Formulating Mathematical Conjectures

Circle the letter of the correct answer.

1. Which of the following is a counterexample of the conjecture "$2x > x$ for all real numbers, x?"

   A. $2 > 1$
   B. $4 < 8$
   C. $-6 < -3$
   D. $10 > -5$

2. Which of the following helps to justify the conjecture that the sum of two even numbers is an even number?

   A. $3 + 5 = 8$
   B. $5 + 4 = 9$
   C. $2 \cdot 4 = 8$
   D. $2 + 4 = 6$

3. Formulate a reasonable conjecture based on the following: $(-1)^2 = 1$, $(-1)^4 = 1$, $(-1)^6 = 1$, $(-1)^7 = -1$

   A. Every power of -1 is 1.
   B. Every odd power of -1 is 1.
   C. Every even power of -1 is 1.
   D. Every power of -1 is positive.

4. Which of the following is a counterexample of the conjecture "If a number is divisible by 4, then it is divisible by 6?"

   A. 12
   B. 24
   C. 48
   D. 64

5. Which of the following helps to justify the conjecture that the product of two even numbers is an even number?

   A. $3 \cdot 5 = 15$
   B. $5 + 4 = 9$
   C. $2 \cdot 4 = 8$
   D. $2 \cdot 3 = 6$

6. Formulate a reasonable conjecture based on the following:

number of sides of a polygon	3	4	5	6	7	8	9
number of diagonals	0	2	5	9	14	20	?

   The number of diagonals of a 9-sided polygon is

   A. 25
   B. 26
   C. 27
   D. 28

7. Which of the following is a counterexample of the conjecture "If a quadrilateral has four equal sides, then it is a square?"

   A. 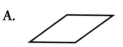   C.

   B. ☐   D. ▭

8. Which of the following helps to justify the conjecture that the product of an even number and an odd number is an even number?

   A. $3 \cdot 5 = 15$
   B. $3 \cdot 4 = 12$
   C. $4 \cdot 6 = 24$
   D. $2 + 3 = 5$

9. Formulate a reasonable conjecture based on the following:

$9 \cdot 2 = 18,$ $1 + 8 = 9$
$9 \cdot 7 = 63,$ $6 + 3 = 9$
$9 \cdot 22 = 198,$ $1 + 9 + 8 = 18$

A. 9 is a prime number.

B. The product of 9 and any number is odd.

C. If a number is multiplied by 9, the sum of the digits in the product is divisible by 9.

D. The sum of 9 and any number is divisible by 9.

10. Which of the following is a counterexample of the conjecture "If a quadrilateral has four equal angles, then it is a square?"

A.    C.

B.   D.

11. Which of the following is a counterexample of the conjecture "$x^3 > x$ for all real numbers, x?"

A. $x = 1$

B. $x = 2$

C. $x = 3$

D. $x = 4$

12. Which of the following helps to justify the conjecture that the difference of two even numbers is an even number?

A. $6 + 4 = 10$

B. $6 - 4 = 2$

C. $6 \cdot 4 = 24$

D. $5 - 3 = 2$

13. Formulate a reasonable conjecture based on the following: $(-1)^3 = -1, (-1)^5 = -1,$ $(-1)^7 = -1, (-1)^8 = 1$

A. Every power of -1 is -1.

B. Every odd power of -1 is -1.

C. Every even power of -1 is -1.

D. Every power of -1 is negative.

14. Which of the following is a counterexample of the conjecture "If a number is divisible by 3, then it is divisible by 6?"

A. 3

B. 12

C. 24

D. 48

15. Which of the following is a counterexample of the conjecture "For any positive integer, n, $n^2 + n + 11$ is prime?"

A. $n = 1$

B. $n = 3$

C. $n = 5$

D. $n = 10$

16. Formulate a reasonable conjecture based on the following: $3 \cdot 4 > 3 + 4, 4 \cdot 5 > 4 + 5,$ $3 \cdot 6 > 3 + 6, 4 \cdot 7 > 4 + 7$

A. $xy > x + y$, if x and y are integers greater than 2

B. $x + y > xy$, if x and y are integers greater than 2

C. $x + y = xy$

D. $x + y > xz$

17. Which of the following is a counterexample of the conjecture "$xy > x + y$, where x and y are integers?"

A. $x = 4, y = 6$

B. $x = -4, y = -6$

C. $x = 2, y = 0$

D. $x = 2, y = 3$

Lesson 59: Formulating Mathematical Conjectures

Applying Inductive and Deductive Reasoning

LESSON 60

You will learn how to:
* use inductive reasoning and deductive reasoning to form conclusions

Key Words: inductive reasoning, deductive reasoning, conditional statement

The process of reaching a conclusion based on information is called reasoning. *Inductive reasoning* is a type of reasoning that leads to a conclusion based on a pattern of examples or events.

Example: 4,560 is divisible by 10.
300 is divisible by 10.
1,999,970 is divisible by 10.
Use inductive reasoning to draw a conclusion.

Look for something that is true in each instance.
Each number is divisible by 10 and each number is even.
Conclusion: All numbers that are divisible by 10 are even.

A conclusion reached by inductive reasoning may not be true.

Example: 4,560 is divisible by 5.
300 is divisible by 5.
1,999,970 is divisible by 5.
Use inductive reasoning to draw a conclusion.

Conclusion: All numbers that are divisible by 5 are even.
This conclusion is false; a counterexample is 25. The number 25 is divisible by 5, but is not even.

The next example is based on a pattern of events.

Example: One day, Mai dropped a bottle of carbonated soft drink. When she opened it, the soft drink sprayed out of the bottle. The next day, after a bumpy ride home from the grocery store, she opened another bottle of carbonated soft drink that she had bought, and the soft drink sprayed out of the bottle. Based on these events, what is a logical conclusion?

Conclusion: Carbonated soft drink will spray out of the bottle if the bottle is opened soon after it is agitated.

Deductive reasoning is a process of reasoning logically from given facts to a conclusion.

A statement in the form "If ...p...., then ...q...." is called a *conditional statement*. The letter "p" represents the statement of given facts, and the letter "q" represents the conclusion.

If a conditional statement is established as true, you can use deductive reasoning to prove a related statement.

Example: If you are in California, then you are in the United States. What related statement can you prove from this true statement?

If the given statement is true, then the following statement is true: If you are not in the United States, then you are not in California.

You can use deductive reasoning to construct a chain of conditional statements and draw a conclusion.

Example: If Tanya is rested before class, she will be alert.
If Tanya is alert, she will pay attention.
If Tanya pays attention, she will pass the quiz.
If Tanya did not pass the quiz, what can you conclude?

Conclusion: Tanya was not rested before class.

The deductive reasoning is as follows:

If Tanya did not pass the quiz, then she did not pay attention.
If Tanya did not pay attention, then she was not alert.
If Tanya was not alert, then she was not rested before class.

Self-Test

Circle the letter of the correct answer.

When Greta ate peanuts, she became ill. When Greta ate an almond bar, she got sick again. What can be concluded, based on the information?

A. Greta gets sick when she eats nuts.

B. Peanuts are dangerous to anyone with a food allergy.

C. Greta is allergic to candy.

D. Almonds are not nuts.

Check your answer.

A is correct.

Greta became ill each time she ate nuts.

Practice

Applying Inductive and Deductive Reasoning

Circle the letter of the correct answer.

1. If $x = 2$, then $x^2 = 4$. What can you conclude based on the information?

   A. If $x \neq 2$, then $x^2 \neq 4$.
   B. If $x^2 = 4$, then $x = 2$.
   C. If $x^2 = 4$, then $x \neq 2$.
   D. If $x^2 \neq 4$, then $x \neq 2$.

2. Paul eats fruit. He is on a diet. He has not broken his diet. What can you conclude based on the information?

   A. Fruit is included on Paul's diet.
   B. Fruit is not included on Paul's diet.
   C. Fruit is good to eat if you are on a diet.
   D. Fruit is a not good to eat if you are on a diet.

3. If it rains, then I take an umbrella to work. I did not take an umbrella to work Saturday. What can you conclude based on the statement?

   A. I walked to work on Saturday.
   B. It did not rain on Saturday.
   C. It rained on Saturday.
   D. I did not watch the weather report on Saturday.

4. If Yoshi does not buy new jeans, he will wear his old ones. If Yoshi does not wear his old jeans, what can you conclude?

   A. Yoshi needs new jeans.
   B. Yoshi did not buy new jeans.
   C. Yoshi bought new jeans.
   D. Yoshi has enough money to buy new jeans.

5. If the bookshelf is full, then David will put books on the floor. David did not put books on the floor. What can you conclude, based on the statement?

   A. The bookshelf is full.
   B. The bookshelf is almost full.
   C. The bookshelf is empty.
   D. The bookshelf is not full.

6. The design on a painting is made up of only rectangles. A square is a part of the design. What can you conclude based on the information?

   A. All rectangles are squares.
   B. The design is only made up of squares.
   C. The square is also a rectangle.
   D. Triangles may be included in the design.

7. If the water is not boiled, then it will not be safe to drink. What can you conclude if the water in the bottle is safe to drink?

   A. The water in the bottle was boiled.
   B. The water in the bottle was not boiled.
   C. The water in the bottle has fluoride.
   D. The water in the bottle is from a natural spring.

8. On Monday, the mail came at 3 P.M. On Tuesday, the mail came at 3:15 P.M. On Wednesday and Thursday, the mail came at 2:55 P.M. What conclusion can you state, based on the information?

   A. The mail will come in the morning on Friday.
   B. The mail will come around 3 P.M. on Friday.
   C. The postal carrier does a good job.
   D. The post office is not busy in the afternoon.

9. Vicki turned in her essay on Tuesday. She did not turn it in late. What can you conclude based on the information?

   A. The deadline for the essay was on Tuesday.

   B. The deadline for the essay was on Wednesday.

   C. The deadline for the essay was not before Tuesday.

   D. The deadline for the essay was not before Thursday.

10. Rachel talked on her cordless phone for 2 hours and the battery went dead. She charged the battery, talked for 2 more hours and the battery went dead again. After a second charge, the battery again went dead after 2 hours. What conclusion can you state, based on the information?

    A. Rachel will get a new battery.

    B. Rachel talks on the phone too much.

    C. The battery in Rachel's phone will last for about 2 hours if she charges it again.

    D. The phone Rachel is using should be replaced.

11. Alan saw a movie that was rated PG-13. Alan only watches movies that his mother allows him to watch. What can you conclude based on the information?

    A. Alan's mother allows him to watch some movies that are rated PG-13.

    B. Alan's mother should let him watch all movies.

    C. Alan's mother allows him to watch all movies that are rated PG-13.

    D. Alan's mother doesn't watch movies.

12. Joe studied for his spelling test and made an A. Joe studied for his science test and made an A. Joe studied for his Spanish test and made an A. What can be concluded, based on the information?

    A. Joe is a good student.

    B. Joe should not study for his next test.

    C. Joe will make an A on his next test.

    D. If Joe studies for a test, then it is likely that he will make an A.

13. If I do not pay the bill, the newspaper will not be delivered. The newspaper was delivered yesterday. What can you conclude based on the statement?

    A. I paid the bill.

    B. The newspaper was wet.

    C. I did not pay the bill.

    D. The newspaper did not come.

14. If you misbehave, you will lose a point. If you lose a point, you will not get a treat. If you get a treat, what can you conclude?

    A. You misbehaved.

    B. You lost a point.

    C. You have 45 points.

    D. You didn't misbehave.

15. If I have the car, then I will pick you up to go to the store. I did not pick you up to go to the store. What can you conclude, based on the statement?

    A. I did not have the car.

    B. I did not go to the store.

    C. I had the car.

    D. I had the car, but I do not like you.

Glossary

A

Absolute value a number's distance from zero: if x is positive, $|x| = x$; if x is negative $|x| = -x$ (1)

Absolute value equation an equation with an algebraic expression in absolute value symbols (22)

Absolute value inequality an inequality with an algebraic expression in absolute value symbols (23)

Add combine to form a sum (2)

Annual interest rate the percent used to find the amount of interest after one year (5)

Area a measure of the surface a two-dimensional figure covers (35)

B

Back-to-back stem-and-leaf plot A representation of two distinct sets of data using place value (53)

Base a number or expression that is used as a factor; an exponent is written to the upper right of the base to indicate how many times the base is used as a factor (7)

Bias a tendency to influence the data (54)

Box-and-whisker plot a display that shows how the data in a set are distributed (53)

C

Circumference the distance around a circle (39)

Claim a statement presented as a fact (54)

Coefficient the numerical factor of a monomial (15)

Commission an amount of money earned, based on the amount sold (5)

Complement all the outcomes that are not part of an event (55)

Compound event an event consisting of more than one outcome (56)

Compound inequality two or more inequalities combined into one, used to represent a set of conditions (12)

Compound interest a percent of the amount in an account, which includes the original amount of the deposit and any interest that the account has earned (5)

Conditional statement a statement in the form "If ..., then ..." (60)

Conjecture a statement that has not been proven true or false (59)

Congruent figures figures with the same shape and same size (44)

Coordinate plane a plane containing two axes that intersect to form a right angle; it allows a method of associating any ordered pair of numbers with a distinct point on the plane (24)

Correlation the general relationship between two sets of numerical data (52)

Corresponding parts the pairs of matching sides or angles of congruent or similar figures (49)

Counterexample any example that proves a conjecture false (59)

Cross-multiply to multiply the numerator of each fraction in a proportion by the denominator of the other (18)

Cube a rectangular prism with six congruent, square faces (44)

Cubic units units used to express measurements of volume (35)

Customary system a system of measurement used in the United States (34)

Cylinder a three-dimensional figure with a curved surface and two congruent parallel bases that are circles (44)

D

Data a collection of facts or information (50)

Deductive reasoning a process of reasoning logically from given facts to a conclusion (60)

Dependent events events for which the occurrence of one affects the probability of the other (56)

Diameter the length of a segment that joins two points of a circle and passes through the center (39)

Direct variation a relationship defined by an equation of the form $y = kx$, where k is a nonzero constant (37)

Discount the amount saved when an item is on sale for less than the regular price (5)

Distribute multiply each term of a polynomial by a factor (16)

Divide determine how many times a number is contained in another number (3)

E

Element a single member of a data set (50)

Elimination method an algebraic method of solving a system of equations by eliminating a variable (30)

Equation a statement that two quantities are equal (11)

Event an outcome or group of outcomes (55)

Exponent a raised number indicating how many times a base is used as a factor (7)

Expression a combination of any or all of the following: numbers, variables, and operation symbols (11)

G

Generalize decide how to apply what you have learned to other cases (57)

H

Hypotenuse the side opposite the right angle in a right triangle (48)

I

Image the figure that results from a transformation (42)

Independent events events for which the occurrence of one does not affect the probability of the other (56)

Inductive reasoning a type of reasoning that leads to a conclusion based on a pattern of examples or events (60)

Inequality a statement formed by placing an inequality symbol between two expressions (12)

Inequality symbol a symbol used to order or compare two quantities (12)

Infinite too many to count (19)

Interest money earned by a person or business who lends money to another person or business (5)

Irrelevant unnecessary (57)

L

Lateral area area of a prism or cylinder not included in the bases (44)

Least common multiple smallest value that a group of numbers will divide into and have no remainder (2)

Legs the two sides of a right triangle that form the right angle (48)

Like terms terms that contain the same variables raised to the same powers (15)

Line graph a graph in which data are represented by points, and the points are connected by line segments (28)

Linear equation an equation with one or more variables, each of which is raised to the first power (17)

Linear equation in two variables a linear equation with two unlike variable terms (24)

Linear inequality an inequality with one or more variables, each of which is raised to the first power (19)

Lower quartile the median of all the data less than the median of a set (51)

M

Markup the amount added to the cost of an item to get the selling price (5)

Maximum the greatest value in a data set (51)

Mean the sum of data elements divided by the number of elements in the data set (50)

Median the middle element or the mean of two middle elements when the data are arranged in increasing or decreasing order (50)

Metric system a system of measurement based on the decimal system (34)

Minimum the least value in a data set (51)

Mode the element in a data set that appears most often (50)

Monomial a number, a variable, or a product of numbers and/or variables (15)

Multiply repeated addition of the same number (3)

N

Negative number a number less than zero (1)

Net a pattern that can be folded to make a three-dimensional shape (44)

Number line a line used to order numbers by associating every number with a distinct point on the line (1)

O

Opposites a pair of numbers that are the same distance from zero and on opposite sides of zero on a number line (1)

Order of operations a set of instructions for simplifying an expression (13)

Ordered pair a pair of numbers for which order matters (24)

P

Parabola U-shaped curve (33)

Parallel lines two lines in a plane that do not intersect (27)

Percent per one hundred (4)

Percent of decrease the ratio of the amount of decrease of a quantity to the original amount, written as a percent (6)

Percent of increase the ratio of the amount of increase of a quantity to the original amount, written as a percent (6)

Perfect square a number whose square root is a whole number (9)

Perimeter the distance around a polygon (39)

Pi (π) the ratio of the circumference of a circle to its diameter; it has an approximate value of 3.14 (39)

Polynomial a monomial or a sum of monomials (15)

Positive number a number greater than zero (1)

Power the result indicated by an expression that contains a base and an exponent (7)

Preimage the original figure before a transformation (42)

Prime factor a factor that is a prime number (2)

Probability the ratio of favorable outcomes to possible outcomes for an event; $P(E) = \frac{\text{Number of Favorable Outcomes}}{\text{Number of Possible Outcomes}}$ (55)

Profit an amount of money earned by a person or business (5)

Proportion a statement that two ratios are equal (18)

Pythagorean theorem in a right triangle, the sum of the squares of the lengths of the legs equals the square of the length of the hypotenuse (48)

R

Radius the length of a segment that joins the center of a circle to a point on the circle (39)

Rate a ratio that compares two quantities expressed in different units of measure (36)

Ratio a comparison of two numbers by division (47)

Rectangular prism a three-dimensional figure with six faces, two of which are congruent, parallel rectangles (44)

Reflection a transformation that results in a mirror image (42)

Right triangle a triangle with a right angle (90°) (48)

Rise the vertical change from one point to another on a line (26)

Run the horizontal change from one point to another on a line (26)

S

Sale price price of an item after the discount has been subtracted from the regular price (5)

Sample space the set of all the possible outcomes (56)

Scale drawing an illustration of an object in proportion to its actual measurements (38)

Scale the ratio that compares the measurements in the drawing or model to the actual measurements (38)

Scale factor the ratio of the corresponding dimensions of two similar figures (47)

Scatterplot a representation of two sets of numerical data on a graph using points (52)

Scientific notation a shorthand method of writing a number as a product of a number and a power of ten (10)

Similar figures figures that have the same shape; the ratios of all corresponding dimensions are equal (47)

Simple interest a percent of the original deposit or loan amount (5)

Simplify write an algebraic expression without negative exponents and with as few exponents, grouping symbols, and operation symbols as possible (14)

Slope the ratio of the rise to the run of a line (26)

Slope-intercept form $y = mx + b$, where m = slope and b = y-intercept (26)

Solution a number that makes an equation or inequality true (17)

Solution set the set of all the solutions to an equation or inequality or system (19)

Square the second power of a number (9)

Glossary

Square root a number which when multiplied by itself, results in the given number (9)

Square units units used to express measurements of area (35)

Statistics the study of data by means of collecting, organizing, and analyzing (54)

Stem-and-leaf plot the display of a set of data organized by place value (53)

Substitution method an algebraic method of solving a system of equations by substituting an expression for a variable (30)

Subtract deduct one value from another (2)

Surface area the total area of the outside of a three-dimensional figure (44)

Survey a method of collecting data in which a group of people is asked one or more questions (54)

System of equations consists of two or more equations (11)

System of inequalities consists of two or more inequalities (12)

T

Term a monomial expression in a polynomial (15)

Transformation a change in the position or appearance of a figure (42)

Translate write a verbal phrase or statement as an expression, equation, or inequality (21)

Translation a transformation that can be thought of as a slide (42)

Tree diagram a display of possible outcomes (56)

Trends patterns of change over time (28)

U

Unit rate a rate in which the number in the denominator is 1 (36)

Unlike terms terms with different variables or different powers of the same variable (15)

Upper quartile the median of all the data greater than the median of a set (51)

V

Valid logically based on the data (54)

Variable a letter or symbol that represents one or more numbers (11)

Vertex the highest point on a parabola if the parabola opens down; the lowest point on a parabola if the parabola opens up (33)

Volume a measure of the space a three-dimensional figure occupies (35)

X

x-intercept the x-coordinate of a point where a graph crosses the x-axis (25)

Y

y-intercept the y-coordinate of a point where a graph crosses the y-axis (25)

Z

Zero the number that separates positive and negative numbers (1)